Rapport Studios

GESSNER GOODRICH HAWLEY was born in Glens Falls, New York, in 1905 and was graduated from Harvard University with an A.B. degree in 1927. After two years of teaching Latin and English literature in the Winthrop (Maine) High School, he spent seven years with a Boston firm in experimental laboratory work.

In addition to some book reviewing and an article on the electron microscope which appeared in the *New Republic*, Mr. Hawley is the author of *Seeing the Invisible*, the story of the electron microscope, and collaborated in the writing of books, *We Need Vitamins* and *Energy in War and Peace*. present Chief Technical E Reinhold Publishing Co

ALSO BY

GESSNER G. HAWLEY

SEEING

THE INVISIBLE

The Story of the *Electron Microscope*

THIS IS A BORZOI BOOK
PUBLISHED IN NEW YORK BY
ALFRED A. KNOPF

Small Wonder

Small Wonder

The Story of *Colloids*

BY

GESSNER G. HAWLEY

ALFRED A. KNOPF   *NEW YORK*

1947

THIS IS A BORZOI BOOK,
PUBLISHED BY ALFRED A. KNOPF, INC.

FIRST EDITION

TO MY SONS GEORGE AND JAMES

THIS BOOK IS LOVINGLY

DEDICATED

Preface

Attempting to present colloid chemistry in a direct, intelligible, and yet reasonably comprehensive way, so that the result will be of value to those who have the curiosity but lack the time to study more erudite treatises, reminds me of the problem that confronted two famous characters of fiction on a memorable stroll by the seashore:

The Walrus and the Carpenter were walking close at hand;
They wept like anything to see such quantities of sand.
"If seven maids with seven mops swept it for half a year,
Do you suppose," the Walrus said, "that they could get
it clear?"
"I doubt it," said the Carpenter, and shed a bitter tear.

There is such a thing as having an embarrassment of subject matter, which it seems quite hopeless to straighten out and organize. The panorama spread before us by this fascinating but somewhat subtle topic is truly enormous. To include even its salient features in a volume of moderate size is almost impossible—for one thing, because there is no general agreement as to what these features are. With enzymes to right of us, cell membranes to left of us, and emulsions ahead of us we probe our way forward, with new and unexpected phenomena cropping up on every hand. It is easy to become bewildered and get lost in it all.

One ever-present bugaboo in such an undertaking is

the extent to which an explanation should be carried in order to justify the name. If you ask a child why it rains, he will probably say something about the clouds turning to water, which is true enough, but not quite a Grade A explanation. A well-informed adult will tell you that evaporation from the surface of oceans and lakes forms water vapor, which condenses under appropriate temperature conditions; he may also add that evaporation is caused by the rapid movement of water molecules, as a result of which a few are expelled from the liquid to form water vapor. This is probably an adequate explanation of the cause of rain. Yet the research scientist would push it one step further; armed with a formidable array of charts and equations, he would go into great detail about intermolecular forces in the water, mean free paths of molecules, kinetic energy, and a host of other abstruse matters.

Obviously I must agree to "freeze" my level of explanation in this book, and I propose to do so at the median or adult level, being perfectly well aware that trained physical chemists could charge me with not having really "explained" anything. Not even *they* can give the ultimate and final answers; but their refusal to be satisfied with explanations which go only part of the way is the key to all scientific progress.

I owe and gratefully extend thanks to many for the assistance and counsel they have extended me in the preparation of this book—in particular to Dr. R. L. Wakeman, Director of Research of the Onyx Oil and Chemical Company, to Dr. Melville Sahyun, Vice-President of the Frederick Stearns Company, to Dr. Eskel Nordell of the Permutit Company, and to Jerome

Alexander, the dean of writers on colloid chemistry, all of whom read portions of the manuscript and contributed many helpful suggestions. I am indebted to the Reinhold Publishing Corporation for permission to reproduce illustrations from several of their books; in all cases where the publisher of a volume is not specifically named in the credit line, the source is Reinhold.

If this book contributes to a more general understanding of colloids or leads to a perusal of more competent and thoroughgoing works on the subject, my hopes will have been well served.

GESSNER G. HAWLEY

New York, N. Y.
January 30, 1947

Contents

Small Wonder

PLATE I *A portion of an installation used to crack petroleum with the aid of a colloidal catalyst.*

From Alexander: *Colloid Chemistry*, Vol. V

PLATE II   *How a sneeze looks to the camera. Forty thousand droplets are tossed into the air by an energetic sneeze. Here is a dark-field picture made by an exposure of 1/30,000th of a second. As the droplets evaporate, the germs which "ride" upon them are left in the air; such suspensions of water in air are called "infective aerosols." There are well over 100,000 bacteria in every sneeze.*

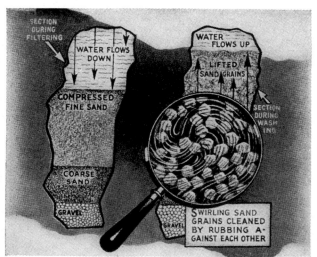

From Dickey & Bryden: *Theory and Practice of Filtration*

PLATE III   *A simple sand filter. As shown at the left, the water passes downward, first through fine sand, then through coarse sand, and finally through gravel. To clean the accumulated dirt from the solid particles, the flow may be reversed, as indicated at the right.*

PLATE IV   *Andromeda—a spiral nebula. It would take light several thousand years to travel from one edge of the spiral to the other.*

PLATE V   *The diffuse type of nebula in Orion, largely composed of incandescent gases.*

PLATE VI *The electron microscope recently built under the direction of Professor E. F. Burton at the University of Toronto. The operator shown is Mr. Grantley Woodward, who carried out most of the actual construction.*

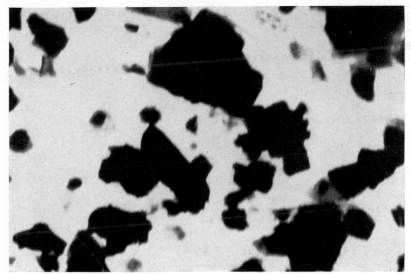

PLATE VII   *Mine dust from blasting operations (magnified 14,000 times). Note the angular, jagged edges.*

PLATE VIII   *The edge of a particle of pollen dust magnified 21,000 times. As one observer remarked, it looks something like a floating mine.*

PLATE IX *An installation for precipitating the suspended impurities in water. The chemicals are fed in through the pipe which empties into the rectangular channel. Uniform feed is insured by baffle plates set at 45° angle in the channel.*

From Dickey and Bryden: *Theory and Practice of Filtration*

PLATE X *Vacuum drum rotary filters. The solid material removed from the water clings to the surface of the drums and is removed by scrapers.*

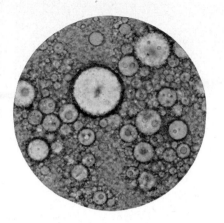

PLATE XI *An emulsion (left) before and (right) after being passed through a colloid mill, or homogenizer, which has the effect of making all the particles the same size. Milk treated in this way remains of uniform consistency, instead of separating into cream and skim milk.*

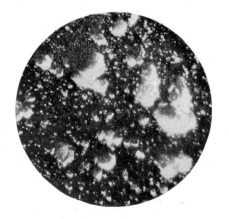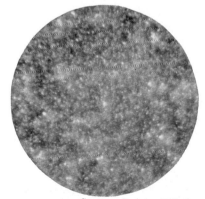

PLATE XII *Pigments (left) before and (right) after being passed through a colloid mill. This technique is useful in the manufacture of paints, inks, and dyes, as well as of compounded latex products.*

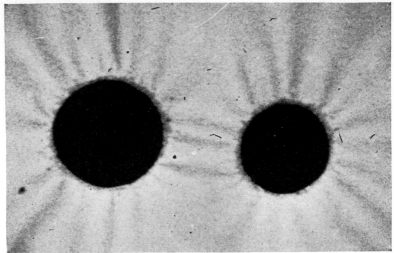

PLATE XIII *Natural latex particles as they appear in the electron microscope (magnified 25,000 times). Compare the size with particles of synthetic latex below.*

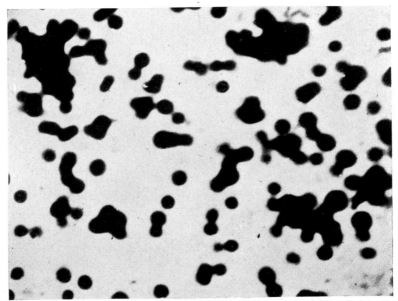

PLATE XIV *Synthetic latex particles as seen in the electron microscope (magnified 25,000 times).*

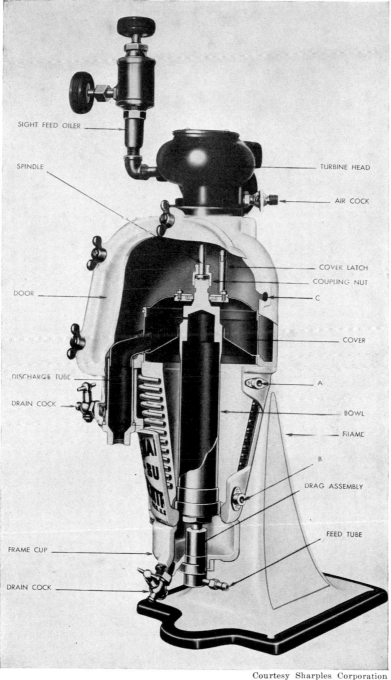

SIGHT FEED OILER

SPINDLE

TURBINE HEAD

AIR COCK

DOOR

COVER LATCH

COUPLING NUT

C

COVER

DISCHARGE TUBE

A

DRAIN COCK

BOWL

FRAME

B

DRAG ASSEMBLY

FEED TUBE

FRAME CUP

DRAIN COCK

PLATE XV *Cutaway view of an ultracentrifuge. Capable of attaining a speed of 50,000 r.p.m., such a machine can separate the components of blood, and is widely used for this purpose in biological and medical research.*

PLATE XVI *Applying liquid resin adhesive to thin layers of wood, called veneers.*

PLATE XVII *Preparing wood veneers for lamination, or sticking together sandwich-wise.*

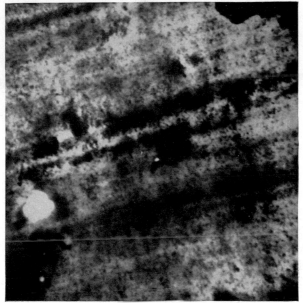

PLATE XVIII *What the inside of a tire tread looks like. Pepper-like specks of carbon black dispersed in vulcanized rubber, as seen by the electron microscope. The total surface area of the black in an average tire tread is in excess of fifty acres.*

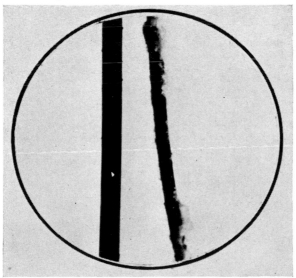

PLATE XIX *A soap-washed hair on the right and one washed with alkyl sulphate on the left. Notice how the soap film clings to the hair on the right while the one washed in alkyl sulphate is clean.*

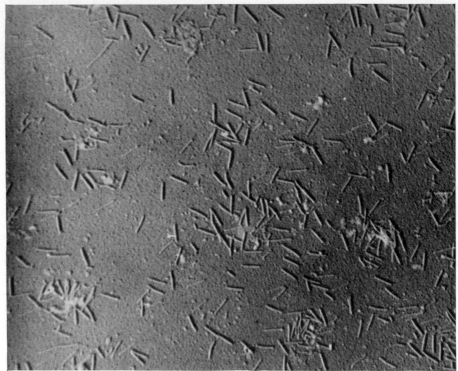

From Alexander: *Colloid Chemistry*, Vol. V

PLATE XX *Tobacco mosaic virus. Each streak is a single macromolecule, and is considered to be a living unit.*

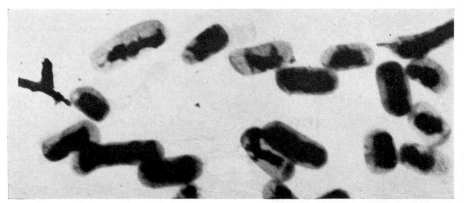

Courtesy University of Toronto

PLATE XXI *The so-called* Bacillus prodigiosus, *magnified 16,500 times by the electron microscope. Note the inner structure revealed by chemical staining.*

CHAPTER 1

What It's All About

o   o
o

COLLOID CHEMISTRY affects everybody unceasingly from the instant of conception until rigor mortis sets in. So manifold are the points at which it touches daily life that merely to enumerate them would be a sizable task. We have to do with it whenever we

> wash our hands
> fry an egg
> sneeze or cough
> butter our toast
> drink a glass of water
> attach a stamp to an envelope
> have a cold
> ride in an automobile
> paint our kitchen
> eat a meal
> draw breath.

Some of its fundamental principles discovered eighty-three years ago were applied successfully to the production of the first atomic bomb.

It was at about the turn of the century that colloid chemistry really began to come into its own. The body of knowledge that has been amassed since then is tremendous indeed. It is still largely confined to specialists,

3

but the time has come when one of the most fruitful and potentially valuable fields of modern science should be at least high-lighted for the general reader.

Like most of the important discoveries of science, the essentials of colloid chemistry are not too difficult to understand, once the jargon which envelops them has been explained. The name itself is enough to scare off the layman. Although accurate from the historical point of view, the word "colloid" is virtually meaningless even to those who are generally well informed; moreover, the subject involves physics even more directly than it does chemistry. To be precise, colloid chemistry may be defined as *the physical and chemical behavior of extremely minute particles in relation to their surroundings.* Those who are approaching it for the first time would do well to forget "colloid" temporarily and cling for dear life to the phrase "extremely minute particles"—for they are the theme of this book.

By way of getting set for a proper take-off, we need to inquire just how small these "extremely minute" particles are, and why their size is of sufficient importance to justify the development of a whole new aspect of science. Attempting to give a correct idea of the order of smallness involved suggests an incident in *Pickwick Papers*, in which the somnolent fat boy is about to impart a shocking revelation to the deaf old lady.

"What do you think I saw in this very arbor last night?" inquired the boy.

"Bless us! What?" exclaimed the old lady, alarmed at the solemn manner of the corpulent youth.

"The strange gentleman—him as had his arm hurt—a-kissin' and a-huggin'—"

"Who, Joe? None of the servants, I hope."

"Worser than that," shouted the fat boy in the old lady's ear.

"Not one of my grand-da'aters?"

"Worser than that."

"Worse than *that*, Joe! Who was it? I insist upon knowing!"

"Miss Rachel," roared the fat boy.

"My da'ater!"

In like manner, when one asks if colloidal particles are as small as bird shot, the reply must be, "Smaller than that!" "As small as pepper grains?" Again, "Smaller than that!" The only way to answer this question intelligibly is by means of a comparison; but it must be carefully drawn and specifically stated.

Let us start with rain. It consists of a vast number of comparatively large drops of water which condense from the vapor-laden atmosphere and fall to the earth by the force of gravity. The size of the drops varies widely with local conditions, from the dimensions of a pinhead to those of a small marble. In the absence of wind, the drops descend vertically, but in a gale they may be driven almost horizontally. The air, of course, offers some opposition to their descent even when there is no wind; to the extent that it does so, it tends to sustain them and to retard their fall. It must be remembered that air has a definite weight and density and is by no means an inert or negligible factor, as the power of violently agitated air in a storm will testify. However, each raindrop weighs so much in comparison with the same volume of air, and the rapidity of its downward motion is so great, that the retarding effect of the air is not of great consequence. The obvious conclusion, then, is just what everyone knows—that *large particles fall by gravity.*

Now suppose we subdivide our raindrop into about a thousand parts. We would then have particles of water so small that they could be seen only in a microscope; and the presence of billions of such particles in the air would be called a fog. Here again there is a wide range of sizes: some fogs are composed of drops so large that they can be distinguished with the naked eye; in others, of the "pea soup" variety (which can almost be cut with a knife, as the saying is) the droplets are much smaller—so small in fact that they tend to remain suspended in the air. The explanation of this strange behavior, which seems contrary to the law of gravitation, will have to be deferred to a later chapter. It is a fact, however, that the smaller the particles, the less is their tendency to settle out; those which are so very small that they cannot be seen even in powerful microscopes will not fall until their balance is disturbed by some external agency. From this illustration of tiny water droplets in the air it is evident that *very small particles do not fall by gravity, but may remain suspended indefinitely.*

But water may exist in air in still another form. We speak of a summer day being humid or "muggy" when it contains a high percentage of water vapor. The capacity of air to "hold" this vapor is appreciable, and it varies considerably with the temperature. At the freezing point of water, it is comparatively small; as a result, cold air is always quite dry. Unfortunately for sea-coast dwellers, the vapor-holding capacity of the air increases sharply between 70 and 80 degrees Fahrenheit—at just the point where summer warmth becomes heat. This abrupt jump, to which we owe the unpleasantness of August "dog days," is a minor instance of what sometimes seems to be the premeditated perversity of nature.

Water vapor is not in the form of droplets, however; it exists as a gas mixed with the oxygen and nitrogen of the air. But even in this form it is composed of particles of water of inconceivable minuteness, much smaller than fog droplets. These particles are called *molecules.* When water evaporates from the surface of a container, a lake, or an ocean, its molecules are taken up by the air; they are separated by relatively great distances and are distributed uniformly throughout the air, regardless of their greater weight. When the number of water molecules in a given volume of air approaches its maximum, condensation occurs whenever there is even a slight drop in temperature. The molecules then unite to form droplets of varying sizes; in a word, the water changes from vapor to liquid. The clouding of the comparatively cool surface of a bathroom mirror is a familiar instance of the precipitation of colloidal water particles. Chemically speaking, water vapor is H_2O, just like liquid water; but physically it represents the final stage to which water can be subdivided. Our third observation, then, is that *particles of one substance may be uniformly dispersed in another in the form of molecules.*

It is a simple matter to draw the same conclusions when water instead of air is used as the medium, and a solid instead of a liquid is considered as the suspended

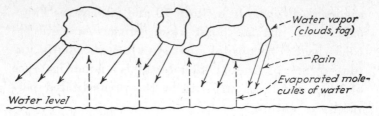

FIG. 1   *Rain is distilled water. The broken arrows indicate water molecules rising from the surface of the sea or lake to form vapor, which condenses into drops under suitable conditions.*

material. For example, if a few grains of ordinary sand are dropped into a tumbler of water, they will float lazily down through the liquid and soon come to rest on the bottom of the tumbler. This combination of sand in water corresponds to the drops of rain in the air just referred to. In both cases the particles—rain in air and sand in water—fall under the influence of gravity, the only retarding effect being the air in one case and the water in the other.

Now let us place in the glass of water a spoonful of a special kind of clay, called *bentonite* because of its discovery near Fort Benton, Wyoming. Stir the mixture well, and let it stand. On returning to it in an hour or so, we can detect no sediment at the bottom of the glass; the presence of the clay is revealed by the smooth, light brown color of the water, but no individual particles are visible. After it has stood overnight, there is still no sediment—nor will there be any for the indefinite future. Here again, as with the fine fog, the earthy clay particles are too small to respond to the pull of gravity; they too will remain suspended until something disturbs their equilibrium. This type of clay is so finely divided that its individual particles are of submicroscopic dimensions—far smaller than those of ordinary coarse clays. Certain forms of sulphur have the same peculiarity.

Having seen that the bentonite suspension is going to stay put, we may now see what can be done to produce a solution comparable to that of water vapor in air, that is, a dispersion of molecules in a liquid. Nothing could be easier: just drop a pinch of sugar into a glass of water. Of course it promptly disappears, or *dissolves*—a word used to denote the separation of a substance into particles of molecular or atomic size. Sugar when dissolved in water is in its ultimate stage of subdivision, namely molecules. These may be broken up into still smaller particles by a chemical reaction, which converts the compound, sugar, into atoms of carbon, oxygen, and hydrogen.

From the foregoing it is evident that there are three very broad classifications of particles in respect to size: (1) those easily visible to the unaided eye, such as raindrops or sand; (2) those which cannot be distinguished even in powerful optical miscroscopes, exemplified by very fine fogs and some types of clay; and (3) molecules of a substance like water or sugar. We are chiefly concerned with particles belonging to the second group. Any substance existing in the form of particles so small that they will not settle out of a solution is called a *colloid*, or is said to be in the *colloidal state*. The molecular particles of group (3), on the other hand, form what are designated as "true solutions."

Coleridge once defined the analytical quality of the human mind as "that false secondary power by which we multiply distinctions." It may seem to the casual observer that the differences just pointed out may be all very interesting, but are of no practical importance except as an exercise in the powers of observation. But scientists do not gratuitously multiply distinctions—they have two most serious purposes in view: to be of direct, practical service to mankind, and to try to attain an ever better understanding of the great secrets of nature. Many of these have not yet been revealed; some may never be. Yet the study of colloid chemistry has contributed some of the most significant advances that have thus far been made toward the fulfillment of these two aims.

Now that a specific meaning for the word "colloid" has been found, the question may be raised: How are these particles of various sizes removed from their respective media? This query is especially pertinent at this point in the development of the subject, because the answer involves some of the characteristic properties of colloidal substances and puts us in immediate touch with their important practical applications.

Coarse particles like sand can be separated from water either by allowing them to settle and then pouring the water off, or by passing the mixture through a piece of ordinary filter paper. The openings in the meshes of the filter paper are too small to allow the particles to go through. There are many types of filters of varying fineness; colloidal particles are so small that they pass through all but the very finest filters.

These processes of sedimentation and filtration are practically applied on a large scale in the purification of drinking water for large towns and cities. The general idea is to draw the water to be purified into huge retaining basins, at the bottom of which is a layer of small pebbles overlaid with a foot or so of sand. As the water stands in this basin the suspended solids, such as mud, clay, and other impurities, settle to the bottom. Since they are too large to force their way between the densely packed sand grains, they remain behind as a layer on top of the sand, while the pure water trickles through the sand and pebbles, free from its burden of impurities. Such an arrangement is known as a *sand filter* (see Plate III).

It should be emphasized that particles of sand and dirt which will settle by their own weight in perfectly still water may be prevented from doing so in water that is in movement, as in a river or even a reservoir. Only when a comparatively small volume of water is set aside does it become quiet enough internally to allow most of the suspended materials to form a sediment by slowly falling to the bottom. The large-scale sand filtering process just described is analogous to the settling of coarse sand in a glass of water, where only gravity is concerned.

Now how about the second case, in which particles of colloidal size must be removed? In the case of the suspension of bentonite in water, the most effective way would be to pour the mixture slowly through a filter made of parchment or collodion. Ordinary filters are useless, because of the minuteness of the particles. But when we are dealing with volumes too big to be handled in a laboratory, other means of removing the colloids must be devised. It should be borne in mind that most of the impurities in water for municipal drinking purposes are in the colloidal state—which means that they cannot be expected to settle out on standing. If it were not for the development of knowledge about colloids and how to handle them, it would be impossible to clarify water and other beverages to the extent that is done today. Beyond stating that the same mechanical set-up is used for this purpose as that just described—that is, the sand filter—we shall have to postpone the answer to the colloid removal question to a later chapter, because it involves a number of considerations which cannot be briefly explained. We have in this great field of purification of liquids—including disposal of sewage, garbage, and industrial wastes—one of the most hygienically valuable uses of colloid chemistry.

The third instance of small particles in a liquid in the form of molecules—a true solution, like sugar in water—requires the use of a totally different process for removal of the substance in solution. The first step in this process involves rapid evaporation of the water, frequently by bringing it to the boiling point. As it changes into vapor, the molecules of the dissolved material are left behind. The vapor, when cooled, condenses into water which is free from the molecules of sugar. If all the water is evaporated off, the solid substance will be left as a crystalline deposit in the container. This procedure is called *distillation;* it takes place on an immense scale in nature in the evaporation of sea-water, which of course eventually becomes rain or snow (see Figure 1). Though the distillation process is widely used in industry, it has nothing directly to do with colloid chemistry. It is interesting to notice, however, that it is a means of removing impurities which are one stage lower than colloids in respect to particle size.

To summarize, we first had coarse particles, removed by filtration through filter paper or sand beds; next came those of colloidal dimensions, separated either by filtration through collodion or over a sand filter by a process to be described later; and finally the removal of molecules in solution by distillation.

It has often been said that colloids are the very stuff of life itself. The fundamental unit of all living matter is the protein molecule. Vast numbers of these combine in complex structures called *cells;* and the process of growth consists essentially of the absorption of nourishment by the cells and their subsequent division to form two new cells. At conception, the embryo comprises the union of one male and one female cell, and all development thereafter until death involves adequate food supply and continual cell division. Individual cells are hardly small enough to be considered as colloidal particles; but the proteins of which they are made definitely are so. Every cell contains a complex mixture of proteins called *protoplasm,* which can be considered the origin of every fundamental change taking place in the life history of a cell. Protoplasm is composed of submicroscopic bits of many kinds of protein substance suspended in water, and therefore falls into the colloidal classification.

Cells contain not only protoplasm, but other protein substances as well. There are the *chromosomes,* which are something like the shell of a pea in which the "peas" are *genes.* It is these tiny specks of matter which are

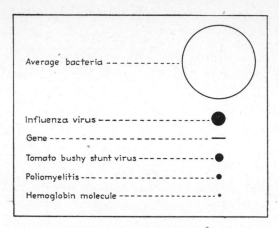

Fig. 2 *Comparative sizes of biological structures. In this and several of the following diagrams, the sizes are of necessity only rough
visual approximations.*

responsible for the transmission of hereditary traits
from one generation to another; and they too are of
colloidal size. An idea of their dimensions can be gained
by referring to Figure 2. Much of the story of genes
and how they work is still unknown. But a realization
of their profound effect on the character traits, intelligence, and capabilities of the individual cannot fail to
bring home to everyone the immense significance of colloids in the marvelous chemistry of life.

During the development of an embryo, how does it
happen that the continual process of cell multiplication
is so purposefully directed? What agency determines
whether one group of cells becomes specifically adapted
to the eye, another group to brain tissue, another to
nerves, another to bony structure, and so on? In short,
how and why are the millions of cells which develop

from the two original ones differentiated by nature, each being adapted for its specific duty in the mature organism? Biologists have long studied this perplexing question, and though some of them have developed ingenious theories, no one really knows the answer. Whether every egg and sperm cell carries all the necessary potentialities within it, or whether the cells become distinguished from one another by some specialized mechanism at an early stage of development of the embryo is still a mystery. The determining factors probably lie in the realm of colloid chemistry.

Thus in many commonplace activities of daily life, in foods, in health, in medicine, and in biology these exceedingly small particles swimming around in liquids or gases assume a significance out of all proportion to their size. In industrial operations too they have many and varied uses, ranging from fuel for stratosphere rockets to pigments for paints. At least two of the major types of chemical reactions which have made possible the development of modern plastics and high-octane aviation gasoline are essentially colloidal in nature: they depend upon the interaction of very small particles under certain condition of temperature and pressure. One of these reactions is the cementing together of rod-like molecules to form a firm, plastic mass, which can then be hardened by heat or by chemicals. This combining process is known as *polymerization*, which in popular language means "making big ones out of little ones."

Both this and other industrially important transformations of matter are made possible by another phenomenon which also involves particles of colloidal dimensions—namely, *catalysis*. To get a clear idea of this situation we must now extend our concept of a particle to include surface irregularities. In this sense a bump on a log and a nick in a razor blade qualify as particles, even though they are, so to speak, parts of larger bodies. It is important to realize that the colloidal state is strictly a matter of dimensions: even a hole is colloidal if it is small enough.

Catalysis has become generally familiar in recent years because of its importance in the manufacture of synthetic gasoline and rubber. Here is a crude illustration of how it works. If a man is standing upright on a wooden plank tilted at a sharp angle, he will slide down extremely slowly, if indeed he moves at all, because of the high friction coefficient between his rough leather soles and the equally rough surface of the wood. But if the wood is covered with an extremely thin coating of grease, his downward motion will be greatly accelerated, or in chemical parlance, catalyzed. Though this analogy might be frowned on by experts, it brings out the basic idea of catalysis, namely, the speeding up of a reaction. It also suggests the colloidal nature of this phenomenon; for the sudden increase of speed is due to what is called a surface wetting effect: molecules of grease cling to and coat all the microscopic wood fibers which together comprise the "roughness" which prevents slippage. Interposing a thin film of grease or oil between two rough, dry surfaces is the basis of lubrication, which involves very small particles and surface irregularities. To return to chemistry for a moment, some substances would require as long to react if left to themselves as it would take the man to slide down the plank—a matter of days, or even weeks; but if a little catalyst is added to the batch, just as the film of grease is placed under our performer's feet, the reaction proceeds quite as suddenly and efficiently. Though the detailed mechanism of catalytic action is not yet wholly understood, it is known to be closely related to the colloidal state of matter.

We cannot here run the gamut of industries in which suspensions of very small particles play a predominant part; some of them will be described later when more of the fundamental background has been sketched in. It should at least be evident from what has been said that colloid chemistry is primarily concerned with particle *size,* and that during the last half century, it has opened the way to a closer approach to the subtle mysteries of life, growth, and reproduction.

CHAPTER 2

Large Things and Small

o   o

o

THE PHYSICAL UNIVERSE can be divided into seven major levels on the basis of size. It must be pointed out, however, that "size" is by no means the same thing as "complexity," which refers to such structures as muscular and nervous systems and all the highly developed mechanisms that characterize living organisms. The tiniest animals have a far more complicated physical structure than huge masses of earth and granite, for example, which in spite of their immensity, are inert and lifeless. This situation is pointed up by the sage remark of the squirrel to the mountain:

> *If I cannot carry forests on my back*
> *Neither can you crack a nut.*

It is true, of course, that there are successive levels of biological complexity as well as of size alone. Since we are first of all attempting to arrive at a correct concept of size relationships, which underlies even an elementary comprehension of colloid chemistry, we might do well to survey the entire universe very quickly, and to note the seven divisions, or size ranges, into which it falls.

The first one requires a big breath and lots of imagination. We may call it the celestial level. Scientists have gained a great deal of knowledge of this level both by direct observations with telescopes and by mathematical processes based upon them. Distances out among the stars are so vast that the only way of measuring them is to use the speed of light as a sort of heavenly yardstick. Light travels at 186,000 miles a second; and the distance it covers in the course of a year at this speed is equal to the fantastic value given by multiplying 186,000 by the number of seconds in a year (31,536,000), which is reasonably close to six *trillion* miles. This little jaunt is referred to as a "light year." Many of the bodies which are clearly visible in a powerful telescope are many thousand light years in *diameter*. Those comprising the Milky Way are about 40,000 light years distant.

Since the introduction and experimental proof of the relativity theory in the early years of this century, physicists and astronomers have come to accept the fact that not only the earth, but the entire universe, including all the stars and the Milky Way, has a shape, and that that shape is roughly spherical. The universe is a much flatter sphere than the earth, however, and approximates the shape of a bulging Ingersoll watch. The distance from one "side" of it to the other is thought to be in the neighborhood of *four billion light years*. If you wish to while away a rainy afternoon by multiplying that figure by six trillion, you will have before you, if the sheet of paper is wide enough, the estimated number of miles of space across the universe.

On this celestial scale, then, we see hundreds of thousands of "stars," at distances from the earth and from each other of hundreds of light years. All these so-called stars (of which the earth is one) are held in unchanging relationships by two forces which act simultaneously. One of these is the universal phenomenon of gravitation. Though the heavenly bodies move in their orbits with extreme rapidity, they behave in strict accordance with the principle that every body in the universe exerts an influence on every other body; the force of this influence, or gravitational attraction, varies with the masses of the bodies and the distances that separate them. Counteracting gravity is centrifugal force; thus the planets are both attracted to and repelled from the sun simultaneously, with the net result that their relative distances from it remain constant. It is indeed an interesting fact that the untold millions of stars hanging in space and kept in their orbits by mutually exerted forces are analogous, on a vast scale, to the colloidal particles of bentonite clay in water and to the fine fog droplets in air described in the first chapter.

Some stars are enormous aggregations of flaming gases with central cores of solid or semi-solid matter; these diffuse stars are called *nebulas* (see Plates IV and V). The solar system, comprising the sun and its nine planets, may have evolved from a nebula by a long process of solidification. The sun, of course, is the original core, and is still in the incandescent state; the planets were very likely torn away from the sun by the close approach of a much larger body and flung off into space. The entire solar system is more than five billion miles in diameter; but, by comparison with the awesome array of the myriads of stars in the Milky Way

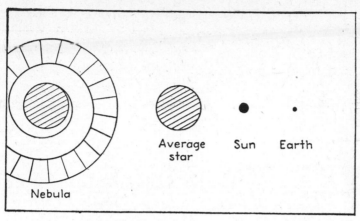

F<small>IG</small>. 3 *Approximate size range at the celestial level.*

and the incomprehensible vastness of interstellar space, it occupies an extremely small part of the universe.

Yet within the solar system, the sun is hundreds of times larger than the earth; it is indeed impossible to find a word that expresses the pinpoint size of this world, which seems so large to us, in the scheme of the universe as a whole. On this level of size, it stands in about the same relation to a nebula as do the molecules of sugar to the grains of coarse sand previously mentioned. This well illustrates the important fact that there is a tremendous range of sizes within each of the seven levels: in the celestial level, this range runs from the largest nebulas at the upper limit to the smallest planets at the lower limit. It will be very helpful to keep these size ranges in mind, and they will frequently be mentioned as we go along.

Next comes what may be called the geographic level of sizes—that is, the earth's crust and all that it con-

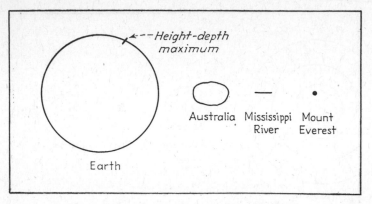

FIG. 4 *Size range at the geographic level.*

tains. Though it is far too large in relation to the individual to be perceived in its entirety, it is small enough to come directly into the range of human experience. We feel that we *know* that the Bay of Bengal and the Kamchatka Peninsula exist, not only because we can find them on a map, but because we could go there ourselves if necessary. Pending the invention of rocket ships, this cannot be said of the planet Mars or the moon, even though we have touched the latter with the fingers of radar.

Here again is a wide range of sizes. The largest, of course, is the globe itself. The smallest is any natural object which cannot be seen fairly completely with the eye under normal conditions; for instance islands, large lakes, and mountain ranges would represent the lower limit of the geographical size group. What a tiny fragment is Wake Island or any of the other volcanic atolls of the Pacific compared with the world as a whole! How small is Lake Geneva on the same scale!

Since man is rather closely limited to the *surface* of

the earth, this is an appropriate point to mention the analogy between it and the surfaces of small particles. The earth's surface is rough—flung up into continents ridged with mountains in some areas, depressed into ocean floors and river valleys in others. Yet the total distance between the deepest ocean and the highest peak is only about eleven miles; on an average this difference in levels does not exceed eight miles. This surface variation is less than 0.25 per cent of the earth's radius, yet it is vitally important for the sustenance of the human race. On a surface wholly free from high plateaus and fairly deep depressions there could be no oceans, no rainfall, no crops—and hence, no life.

Equally vital are the surface irregularities of very small particles. As previously explained, these irregularities are of colloidal dimensions, and are responsible for the highly important phenomenon of catalysis. A perfectly smooth particle would be useless for this purpose. On the geographic scale, mountains and valleys are comparable to the submicroscopic roughness on minute particles of catalytic substances—insignificant compared with the total thickness, but mighty indeed in biological and chemical significance!

It is useful to indicate these broad analogies that occur in nature, for they help us to interpret the vast complexity of the universe in terms of a relatively few major principles, and they indicate the fundamental unity and constancy of natural phenomena. The very word "universe" implies oneness—a oneness that underlies a bewildering diversity.

The next level of size is the most commonplace of all. It comprises everything that we see around us by ordi-

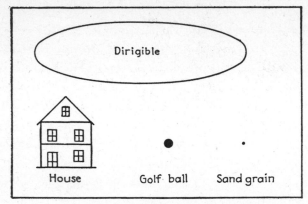

Fig. 5   *Size range at the ocular level.*

nary use of the eyes—from battleships and suspension bridges on the large side to grains of sand or sugar on the small. Obviously here again is a wide range, roughly comparable to those on the celestial and geographic levels. It is pertinent to note also that what we may call the ocular or "eye" level is the upper limit of size for living organisms. The largest animal on earth is the whale, although prehistoric reptiles were considerably larger; but this is far from being the largest object that the eye can take in.

To suggest the practical significance of the sizes of materials, let us imagine that a large pier or wall is to be built out of stones and cement. Three choices are possible: to use very large boulders merely pushed together and chinked with cement; to reduce the size of the boulders by breaking them up and building the wall with the fragments by inserting cement in the crevices; or to grind the smaller stones to fine gravel or pebbles, blend these with cement, and use the mixture. If structural strength is a factor, the third choice is the wisest, for the smaller the pieces of stone and the rougher their surfaces, the more firmly they bind the cement. Here is another example of the importance of the irregularity of surfaces—this time on the ocular level.

The whole concept of colloidal particles and their behavior in general is closely related to the size, shape, and total area of exposed surface. The latter increases rapidly as an object is subdivided. A cubic foot of wood, for example, has an exposed area of six square feet; but if it is cut up into 1728 one-inch cubes, the total area of surface jumps to 72 square feet. Attention will be drawn to the scientific importance of this fact from time to time; at the moment, the crushed stone example will illustrate the principle.

While discussing this familiar size level within which we all live, it will be well to make clear what is meant by "seeing" an object. Scientists usually use the word "resolve" rather than "see;" they consider this more accurate because it better describes the mechanism of visual perception. Contrary to popular ideas, this is the faculty possessed by the eye and all other optical instruments, of picking out or distinguishing one object from another. The smallest particle that the eye can resolve is about 1/250 of an inch in diameter, which means that if two particles are separated by a distance less than 1/250 of an inch, they will appear to be one particle; in other words, the eye cannot resolve or distinguish them as individuals. The same principle applies to telescopes and microscopes, whose great value lies in their ability to extend the limit of resolution of

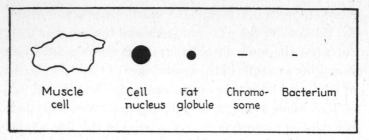

Muscle cell   Cell nucleus   Fat globule   Chromosome   Bacterium

FIG. 6   *Size range at the microscopic level.*

the eye in both directions so tremendously. This brings us to the range of sizes which lies just below the ocular —the domain of microscopic particles.

Solid matter most commonly occurs in the form of crystals. Perhaps the most generally familiar crystal is that seen on window panes in zero weather; they are an excellent instance of the tendency of matter to solidify in rigid interlocking structures. A good reading glass suffices to reveal the intricate designs in snowflakes; but the simplest crystalline forms of quartz and calcium that make up the rocks and pebbles we were just speaking of, as well as those of other common substances like salt and sugar, are well beyond the resolving power of a single lens.

Crystals are only one of many fascinating types of objects revealed by the compound microscope; indeed they are of far less importance than the hundreds of biological structures, precise knowledge of which during the last century has enabled science to make such tremendous advances in medicine and physiology. Typical in respect to size is the cell; though cells vary in dimensions with the type of organism and the location in the body, they are in general large enough to permit detailed examination. Cells are by no means simple structures; they have an outer casing or envelope, within which is the protoplasm. At or near the center of the mass of protoplasm is the nucleus, wherein are located the essential reproductive mechanisms. A hen's egg, in fact, is an overgrown cell whose component parts are visible on the ocular size level: the shell corresponds to the integument of the microscopic cell, the "white" is the colloidal protoplasm, and the yolk is the nucleus. This is another case of parallel structures existing on two different levels of size.

Many simple organisms consist of only one cell; these are low forms of life, such as algae and amoebas. All sorts of bacteria belong in this classification—the common germs of tuberculosis, diphtheria, and other fatal diseases. The virus group, however, is much smaller in size and definitely belongs to the colloidal level.

For all practical purposes, the resolving power of a compound microscope is about 200 times that of the human eye; consequently particles as small as 1/50,-000 of an inch in diameter can be distinguished. It is obvious that the range of microscopic sizes is much smaller than we have found on any of the other levels so far mentioned. Nevertheless, the invention and improvement of microscopes constitutes one of the most important mechanical advances in the history of science, for until the great complex world lying below the ocular level was penetrated, no one could formulate any correct ideas about life and the architecture of nature. It is well worth stressing the fact that, within the biological realm, the levels of size we are attempting to identify are by no means independent of one another: it often happens that what occurs at the microscopic level will have a profound effect on the state of affairs at the next higher level. A swollen gland, for example, would fall in the ocular group, yet it may be caused by infectious organisms of microscopic dimensions.

We come now to the range of sizes which it is the purpose of this book to explain, namely, the colloidal level. Scientists have indulged in a good deal of argument as to the exact upper and lower limits of colloidal sizes. The measuring unit usually applied to such tiny specks is the *micron*; a micron is one thousandth part of a millimeter, or 1/25,000th of an inch. It is pretty generally agreed that the smallest particle that can be considered of colloidal size is about one thousandth of a micron, or one *millimicron*.

As to where the colloidal range stops and the microscopic level starts, there is no such agreement. We shall not attempt to discuss the arguments pro and con; for the purpose of this discussion, any particle less than one-half a micron in diameter will be considered to be of colloidal size. Thus we have a range of particle sizes beginning at half a micron, the point at which the most powerful optical microscopes stop, and running down to one millimicron; or, to keep the units exactly the same, from 500 millimicrons for the largest to 1 millimicron for the smallest. This range of course is even smaller than that of the microscopic level; notwithstanding this, it is of immense significance—for *it is the lowest level of size at which life is found to exist.* This point will be developed in

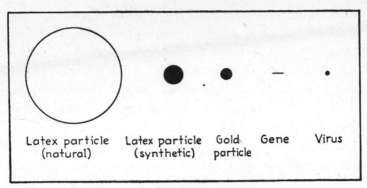

| Latex particle (natural) | Latex particle (synthetic) | Gold particle | Gene | Virus |

FIG. 7   *Size range at the colloidal level.*

subsequent chapters, but at the risk of being repetitious we may paraphrase a cliché and say that "life begins at the colloidal level;" and it not only begins but is maintained there. To back up this statement, here is a list of the more common substances which normally occur in the colloidal state, those most closely related to biological processes being given first:

Viruses	Starch
Genes	Gelatin
Vitamins	Rubber latex
Protoplasm	Carbon black
Blood	Dyes
Milk	Dust and smoke
Egg-white	Fog
Glue	Bentonite clay

As pointed out in Chapter 1, it is dimension, and only dimension, that is involved in colloid chemistry: the chemical nature of the substance is only incidental. It is for this reason that the word "chemistry" is really a misnomer when applied to colloids, for the behavior of particles *as particles*—that is, as aggregates of matter—is actually the primary concern of the science of *physics*. Subject to certain qualifications which will be brought out later, it may be said that *any* substance is a colloid if it is comprised of particles lying in the range of 1 to 500 millimicrons. Gold was prepared in this way centuries ago by the alchemists, and is still used in the colloidal state to color stained glass. When mixed with a quantity of molten glass, it gives a beautiful red product which is often called "ruby glass." Silver is also precipitated in colloidal form on photographic film. Some claims have been advanced for its effectiveness in medicine, and it is known to have specific bactericidal properties.

Strict adherence to the size concept permits us to extend the scope of colloid chemistry to include comparatively rare cases where matter is in such a form that only one of its dimensions is in the colloidal range. It is possible to flatten a piece of gold leaf to the point where its thickness is about half a micron. In such a case it will behave like any other colloid in reference to that dimension. Soap films having a thickness of one molecule have been prepared. We have already spoken of the importance of projections and indentations on larger particles as being within the colloidal domain. We can thus summarize this most vital size level by defining as a colloid any particle, projection, depression, edge, or aperture whose effective dimensions lie within the limits given above.

There are still two size levels to be considered. That immediately below the colloidal range is the *molecular*

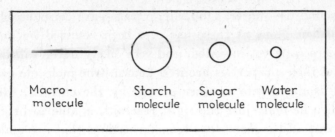

FIG. 8 *Size range at the molecular level.*

level. To this belong particles less than one millimicron in diameter, such as the sugar molecules previously mentioned. It is a characteristic of many chemical compounds—that is, substances composed of two or more elements—to form "true solutions" when dissolved in water or other solvent. In such a solution the compound exists in the form of individual molecules or atoms dispersed among the molecules of the solvent.

There is a vast difference in the sizes of molecules. Some are extremely large and complicated aggregates of carbon, oxygen, nitrogen, and hydrogen arranged in long, chain-like networks. These occur in the group of substances known as *proteins*—constituents of all basic forms of life. Such molecules are so large that they extend up into the range of colloidal dimensions, though from the strictly chemical standpoint they are individual compounds. Because of their unusual size they are known as *macromolecules*, and have been positively identified as such in the tobacco mosaic virus, which is perhaps the primal form of life. Other types of large molecules are cellulose (cotton) and starch.

These huge molecules are the exception, however. Most of the common types that make up the world

around us—water, sand, air, metals—are considerably
smaller. None of these has ever been resolved by any
microscope yet invented, and very likely never will be.
Yet their properties are well known. One molecule can
be changed into another at will by the chemist, who
when he finds just the right reactant, is able to bring
about all the marvelous transformations that are making this more and more a world of synthetic products.
As a general rule, it may be said that the average
colloidal particle is from thirty to fifty times as large
as the average molecule. Since we are primarily concerned with particle sizes, there is no necessity for
going into the chemical characteristics of molecules.

All molecules are built up of atoms, which are bound
together by electrical forces. In view of the startling
progress in nuclear physics in recent years, it is difficult to say with certainty just how many kinds of
atoms there are. Up to 1939, 92 was generally considered to be the correct number; but neptunium (93)
and plutonium (94) were discovered in that year by
Otto Hahn in Germany and Enrico Fermi in the
United States, and the existence of numbers 95, 96,
and 97 was announced in 1945.

On the atomic level, we once more find a breath-
taking size range—not as between the various atoms
themselves, but as between the atom as a whole and its
component parts. Each atom is comprised of a nucleus,
or core, around which revolve a number of electrons,
just as the planets of the solar system revolve around
the sun. Here is a fine example of the parallelism
existing between different size levels in nature. Hydrogen, the simplest atom, has only one electron. This

"weighs" only 1/1835 as much as the nucleus, which is a single proton, and is separated from it by a distance quite comparable to those which separate the heavenly bodies. A rough idea of these distances within the atom is conveyed by the fact that if a hydrogen nucleus were expanded to the size of a pea, the corresponding electron would itself be 30 feet in diameter, and would be about 300 miles away! Yet a hydrogen atom is so infinitesimal that 200 million of them placed side by side would scarcely equal an inch.

Atoms are particles of matter, and so are the smaller units of which they consist. We cannot here enter into a discussion of the basic structure of matter, except to point out that 92 different combinations of protons, electrons, and neutrons have properties which characterize them as elements, such as gold, lead, or calcium, whereas these component units individually can be considered only as particles, or aggregates, of electrical energy. An atom of carbon, for example, contains six protons and six neutrons in its nucleus, around which revolve six electrons. This combination is the smallest particle of carbon that can exist, and results in many specific properties that distinguish carbon from other elements. These are due to the number and arrangement of the basic units, which themselves are particles of energy.

This brief attempt to try on nature for size, so to speak, has shown the strategic location of the colloidal range between the microscopic and the molecular levels. It is here that our attention will be concentrated throughout this book, with an occasional glance above

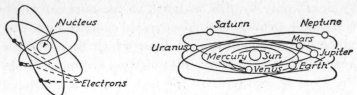

From Hawley: *Seeing the Invisible* (Knopf)

FIG. 9   *The atom is built on the same plan as the solar system:*
the nucleus of the atom corresponds to the sun, the electrons to
the planets.

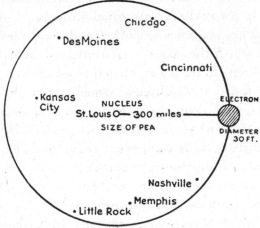

From Bazzoni: *Energy and Matter* (University Society, New York)

FIG. 10   *Lord Rutherford's concept of a hy-*
drogen atom. If the nucleus were enlarged to
the size of a pea, the accompanying electron
would be 30 feet in diameter, and would be
300 miles distant. Its orbit under these imagi-
nary conditions would pass near Little Rock on
the south and Chicago on the north, if the nu-
cleus were located in St. Louis.

or below when necessary. The underlying continuity of
nature will be brought out by a quick comparison of
the drawings in this chapter: it is evident that one

could almost be substituted for another merely by changing the designations. The only real difference is the level or scale of sizes referred to. We have also noted instances of parallel arrangements on different levels: for example, the similarity between atomic structure and the solar system, between the surface irregularity of the earth and that of small particles, and between a hen's egg and a microscopic cell. The stage should now be set to present something of the story of colloid chemistry and its practical significance in daily life.

Summary of Size Levels

Level	Large	Medium	Small
1. Celestial	Nebula	Star	Planet
2. Geographic	Earth	Island	Mountain
3. Ocular	Skyscraper	Football	Sand grain
4. Microscopic	Bacteria	Blood corpuscle	Fat globule
5. Colloidal	Rubber particle in latex	Carbon black particle	Protein molecule
6. Molecular	Cellulose	Sugar	Water
7. Atomic	Atom	Electron	Proton

Chapter 3

The Discovery and Occurrence of Colloids

○ ○

○

SOME COMPETENT AUTHORITIES maintain that it is erroneous to consider colloid chemistry a new branch of science, because the existence of matter in this submicroscopic state was suspected and even asserted as long ago as 1775—at about the time when the chemical elements themselves were being discovered by such men as Joseph Priestley, Antoine Lavoisier, and Sir Humphry Davy. If this is true, they say, how can there be anything particularly new about it? Our reply to this question is that, regardless of the fact that several great scientific minds had thought about the situation, and that one of them at least had conducted definitive experiments which are now regarded as the first basic work in this field, it was not until early in this century that a technique was developed for actual direct observation of colloidal behavior. Once this was done, it became possible to conduct all the experiments necessary to discover the laws governing it, and to apply these to the solution of practical problems in industry and biology.

In a word, though the existence of colloids has been suspected for about 150 years, and was proved about eighty years ago, when organic chemistry was in its infancy, we feel justified in claiming them for a new science because they were not *generally* understood until some forty years ago. And it is the extent to which a subject is known and that knowledge applied that should be the criterion of its length of service to man as a coherent body of information, rather than the conclusions of a few isolated research workers, however great scientists they may have been.

It is extremely difficult to assign any definitive dates to the uncovering of such important areas of knowledge as the various branches of chemistry. However, allowing for considerable overlapping, we may consider that inorganic chemistry began in the neighborhood of 1775, when Priestley discovered oxygen. Organic chemistry, which deals primarily with substances containing carbon, was sufficiently developed by 1823 to justify the publication of a treatise by Gmelin; and five years later the German scientist Wöhler synthesized a compound called urea—the substance which has leaped into prominence in recent years in the field of colored plastics. The possibilities of synthetic organic chemistry were generally appreciated and organic research well under way by 1862, when Graham laid the foundation for colloid chemistry. But it was not until the invention of the ultramicroscope in 1903 that the existence and properties of finely divided particles began to be studied widely and systematically. So, very roughly, we may take 1800 as an approximate date for inorganic chemistry, 1850 for organic chemistry, and 1900 for colloid chemistry —these convenient dates roughly representing the times at which the three subjects had become well established branches of scientific thought and experiment. It is a significant fact in this connection that, although there have for years been many technical journals devoted to the other divisions of science, the first periodical given over exclusively to colloid chemistry—the *Journal of Colloid Science*—made its bow in January 1946.

The point was made in the previous chapter that although certain types of substances, such as albumin, gelatin, and protoplasm, are usually found in the colloidal state, *any* substance above the molecular size level can exist as a colloid if it is divided into sufficiently small particles. It is strange that man's first recorded experience with colloidal substances was with one which is not normally in this form—gold. Away back in the Middle Ages the scientists of the day were known as alchemists. In the light of our present knowledge they are often held up to ridicule because many of their ideas were drawn from long-standing superstitions instead of from experimentally determined facts. They were not quacks or charlatans, however, any more than were their contemporaries, the medieval physicians, who were given to blood-letting as a universal remedy, and who implicitly believed that the positions of the planets in relation to the signs of the zodiac controlled all physiological processes. On the whole, they were serious-minded, sincere men, and should not be blamed for their credulity. They simply didn't know any better. In some respects, we of the twentieth century are as naive as they.

One of the chief goals of the alchemists was to discover a workable method of making gold out of less valuable metals. This achievement was reserved for

two contemporary Harvard professors—R. Sherr and
K. T. Bainbridge—who succeeded in transmuting a few
atoms of mecury into gold with the aid of a cyclotron
in 1941. The alchemists somehow blundered their way
into a method of reducing the particle size of gold to
such an extent that when mixed with water it had the
appearance of liquid gold. The particles were too small
to settle out of the solution, and the result was a
preparation that would remain in suspension indefinitely. They called it *aurum potabile*, or "drinkable
gold." It was found to be of some benefit in certain
types of ailments, either imbibed directly or applied
externally in the form of an ointment. Silver solutions
were prepared in the same way. Today both these
colloidal solutions are known to be helpful in specific
kinds of diseases and to have antiseptic value. Together with aluminum and bronze, they are in standard use as paints for decorative and artistic purposes.
In this case at least, the medieval boys were not so
stupid after all. They did not, of course, know what
they had prepared, nor were they aware that the gold
and silver were in any especially important or unusual
condition. They did not concern themselves with why
the particles showed no tendency to sediment on standing. This was a far cry indeed from making gold out
of lead, but at least it had some practical value.

A French chemist named Macquer was apparently
the first to assert that "drinkable gold" was not a
"true" solution like salt or sugar in water, but one
containing particles much larger than molecules. He
carefully described the solutions prepared by the alchemists in what was probably the first chemical dic-

tionary ever published (1774). A half-century later
Berzelius, a noted Swedish scientist who contributed
greatly to the early history of chemistry, and the
Italian Selmi also concluded, on the basis of their work
with substances like sulphur, casein, and albumin, that
the solutions obtained with these are essentially different from "true" solutions.

About the middle of the nineteenth century the great
English scientist Michael Faraday, whose researches
laid the basis of modern electrochemistry, succeeded
in preparing solutions of colloidal gold and in determining some of their properties. Faraday published a
paper in 1857 describing the results of his findings,
stating that in his opinion these solutions were made
up of gold particles in a fine state of subdivision and
that they possessed unique characteristics. The evidence which he submitted to prove his contention will
be referred to presently.

A few years later came the first really significant
work, which resulted in the actual discovery and nam-
ing of colloids and in establishing their nature. For
this, credit is due to another Englishman, Thomas
Graham, who performed a long and exacting series
of experiments before announcing his findings. Graham's interest centered around solutions and their
tendency to form a uniform, homogeneous mixture
when blended. For example, if two sugar solutions containing very different numbers of sugar molecules are
separated by a membrane of collodion or parchment,
they will after a time become so uniformly blended
that no difference in strength can be detected at any
point. The sugar molecules in the strong solution will

force their way through the tiny holes in the parchment until the number of sugar molecules, or concentration, on both sides of the membrane is identical.

The penetration of molecules through such a "permeable" membrane is called *dialysis,* and the differential force is known as *osmotic pressure.* This is of tremendous importance in biology, for it is the means by which cells receive their nourishment, and is thus an essential factor in growth. Nutritive substances in true solution pass through the membrane which forms the outer protective covering of the cell. This basic growth process occurs in all living tissue, in plants as well as in animals.

The entire group of phenomena involving the passage of molecules in solution through membranes acting as filters is included under the head of *diffusion* in the scientist's notebook. It is obvious that the apertures in the membrane must be slightly larger than the molecules of sugar; otherwise they could not get through. Here is an instance of a hole being in the range of colloidal dimensions. As a matter of fact the holes in parchment—which has a pore structure similar to that of the human skin—are exactly on the line of demarcation between colloidal and molecular sizes —about one-half a micron in diameter.

Thomas Graham was the pioneer investigator of the diffusion process. By careful experimental research (1862) he worked out the mathematical formulas governing the rate at which the diffusion of molecules of both gaseous and liquid solutions occurs; and these have ever since been considered the basis of engineering problems in which diffusion plays a part. One of the

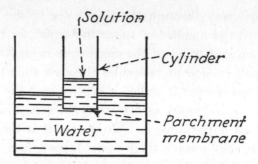

F<small>IG.</small> 11   *Graham's set-up for separating colloids from crystalloids* (*see text for discussion*).

plants erected at Oak Ridge, Tennessee, for separating the very rare atoms of U-235 from the much more numerous atoms of U-238 involved passing the uranium in the form of a gas through porous barriers. The barriers contained literally billions of holes which were just large enough to permit a single uranium atom to pass through; the fact that there was only one atom of U-235 to every 139 of U-238 made it necessary to construct a series or "cascade" of barriers comprising about 4000 units. This astonishing feat of engineering is mentioned here because the fundamental diffusion principles discovered by Thomas Graham were used in solving this baffling problem.

The set-up which Graham used for his observations was very simple. First he placed in a container a quantity of the pure solvent, which was usually water. Then he filled to about half its capacity a glass cylinder, the lower end of which he had covered with a parchment membrane. The liquid contained in this cylinder was a solution of water and the substance whose diffusion characteristics Graham was endeavoring to discover. He then set the cylinder in the bowl of water and held it in such a position that its lower end was an inch or two below the surface, as shown in Figure 11. The theory was, of course, that the dissolved matter in the cylinder would pass through the parchment at a rate depending upon its concentration, until the water in the bowl contained the same proportion of dissolved material as that in the cylinder.

Graham subjected a great variety of substances to this *dialysis* technique. He found that when he had a solution of salt or sugar in the cylinder, both of them invariably turned up sooner or later in the water in the container, but that when he placed a solution of glue or gelatin in the cylinder, not a trace of either was detectable in the water. He concluded from these observations that there are certain types of substances whose particles are too large to penetrate the minute holes in the parchment, and that there are certain other types whose particles can penetrate them. Reasoning on this basis he classified all matter into two general groups: (1) Substances which in solution will pass through a parchment membrane. These he called *crystalloids*, because when evaporated they form aggregates of crystalline solids. Such substances exist as molecules in the solvent, and thus form "true" solutions. (2) Substances whose particles in solution are too large to go through the membrane, and are therefore retained or held back by a parchment filter. Since his early experiments were conducted with solutions of glue in water, he designated materials of class (2) as colloids, a name derived from the Greek word *kolla*

(glue). The same word is found in such terms as collodion and collagen, which also have a sticky, glue-like
consistency when warm. Although Graham was confined to the use of actual parchment for his filter membrane, modern synthetic materials like collodion and
cellophane are now employed in dialysis experiments.
Graham's division of matter into crystalloids and colloids is not as absolute as it sounds, and is subject to
an important qualification, to be mentioned later.
Provisionally, however, it may be accepted at face
value.

So the groundwork of the science of colloid chemistry
was laid by Faraday and Graham in England, at about
the time of the outbreak of our Civil War. The technique established by Graham and his criterion of distinction between molecular solutions of crystalloids and
colloidal solutions of particles much larger than molecules has never been seriously criticized or depreciated.
The importance of thoroughly grasping the various
levels of particle dimensions described in the preceding
chapter is now evident, and it will become still more so
as we go along. Crystalloids have many properties
which colloids do not, and vice-versa. Whether a solution is made up of molecules or atoms, or whether it
contains particles of colloidal dimensions makes all the
difference in the world in its behavior and characteristics—a difference which is of vast practical importance in both biology and industry.

One small but important matter of terminology
should be mentioned before proceeding further. It is
customary in discussing solutions to speak of the

solvent, or the medium in which the material is dissolved, as the *continuous phase* and the substance in solution as the *dispersed phase*. For example, in a colloidal gold solution, the water is the continuous phase and the particles of gold the dispersed phase. Some authors prefer the term "external" to "continuous" and "internal" to "dispersed," but these are likely to cause confusion and therefore will not be used in this book. The medium in which the substance is suspended or dispersed—for example, air or water—is looked upon as being continuous, in the sense that red is the continuous field in a red gingham dress with white polka dots, the latter being analogous to the dispersed phase. The more white dots there are—or in colloidal terms, the higher the concentration of the dispersed material—the more difficult it is to tell whether you have a red dress with white dots or a white dress with red dots. In like manner, when a dispersed material is present in very large quantity in a solution, an inversion of phases may occur, with important effects on the properties of the solution.

After a little contemplation of Graham's distinction between crystalloids and colloids and the concept of continuous and dispersed phases, the scope and complexity of the field covered by colloid chemistry begins to dawn upon one. It may be well to set down a resumé of the various types of colloidal systems that have so far been mentioned, assigning to each the correct designation as to its phase relations. From this summary it may be easy to draw some inferences about other possible systems.

(1) Fog * or mist consists of water droplets suspended in air. Here the continuous phase is gaseous (a
mixture of oxygen and nitrogen) and the dispersed
phase is liquid.

(2) Bentonite clay particles in water form a colloidal solution (the words "solution," "dispersion," and
"suspension" are often used interchangeably in describing the colloidal state). In this case, we have a
solid dispersed in a liquid, the latter of course being the
continuous phase.

(3) Gold, silver, or other metallic substances can be
divided so finely by artificial means that they appear in
the form of colloidal solutions when added to water.
This is another instance of solid particles suspended in
a liquid.

(4) Graham's dispersions of glue and water must
also be classed as solid-liquid systems; but it is obvious
that glue is a far less dense solid than gold.

Everyone knows that there are three forms in which
matter can exist—as a gas, a liquid, or a solid. In view
of the above-mentioned examples of liquid-in-gas and
solid-in-liquid types of dispersions, it would seem to be
a fair guess that any two of these forms may combine
to constitute a colloidal system, and that each of them
can be either the continuous or the dispersed phase. In
the two types mentioned above, (1) a liquid suspended
in a gas and (2) a solid suspended in a liquid, it is clear
that the liquid is the dispersed phase in the first case
and the continuous phase in the second. Is this equally

---

* Some authorities contend that the droplets would have to be
about half the size of the smallest known in nature, to constitute a
true colloid.

true of the other two forms of matter—gaseous and solid?

In case (1) the gas is plainly the continuous phase. If our guess is any good, we should expect to have a system in which a gas is the dispersed phase. This combination does exist, and is encountered rather frequently in froths and foams, for example, in whipped cream or in the "head" on a glass of beer. Even though many of the bubbles may exceed colloidal dimensions, it is perfectly possible for true colloidal systems to exist in this gas-in-liquid form. An excellent instance of this is the presence of submicroscopic bubbles of dissolved nitrogen gas in the blood. This is likely to occur when the body is subjected to abnormal pressure conditions for any length of time. Nitrogen is squeezed out of the tissues into the bloodstream and causes what is commonly known as "bends," which afflicts deep-sea divers and sometimes aviators who have not been properly "decompressed" on returning to sea level. Physicians have named this annoying and sometimes dangerous condition "emphysema." To avoid it, special compartments are provided in which the diver is placed, the atmospheric pressure being gradually reduced over a period which varies with the depth and the time he has been down. Thus the nitrogen colloidally suspended in the blood is slowly dissipated.

Now that we have noted that liquids and gases may be either the continuous or the dispersed phase in specific cases, let us see if this is equally true of solids. We have already noted several examples of solids suspended in liquids, and it is easy to imagine them being dispersed in the air in the form of dust or smoke. But can a solid ever be the continuous phase—can matter be suspended in a solid under any conditions? Very easily. In making cushions or mattresses out of rubber, the milk-like latex is agitated until it foams. In this condition, the rubber is unvulcanized, and we have a system comprising a gas suspended in a liquid. But when the latex foam is poured into a mold and vulcanized, or cured, the rubber becomes a solid. The result is a gas (air) suspended in a continuous phase which, though soft and elastic, is nevertheless a solid. Similarly, sponge rubber is composed of carbon dioxide gas dispersed in vulcanized rubber. So the general statement is justified that any of the three forms of matter may be either the continuous or the dispersed phase of a colloidal system.

But this by no means exhausts the possibilities of phase combinations. Up to this point we have called attention to instances in which the two phases were *different,* such as solid-in-liquid, liquid-in-gas, etc. It is not only possible, but quite normal for a system to have the *same* state of matter in *both* its phases. A solid may be colloidally dispersed in a continuous solid phase. For example, in making automobile tire treads, a large proportion of carbon black is blended with the rubber, and the mixture vulcanized. Carbon black is a pigment and abrasion-resisting agent made by burning natural gas and allowing the flame to strike a metal plate or "channel." The black is deposited in the form of particles of colloidal size. Since rubber is also a solid after it is coagulated from the milky latex, it constitutes the continuous phase of the mixture, and the solid particles of carbon black the dispersed phase. On vulcanization, a suspension of solid particles in a solid continuous medium is obtained—and the world rolls forward on colloidal cushions! Further discussion will be devoted in a later chapter to the interesting, though complex, subject of rubber and carbon black.

Even more common than solid-solid systems are those in which both phases are *liquids*. Many examples of these readily come to mind. Mayonnaise is made up of colloidal droplets of vinegar and olive oil, to which a little egg-yolk is added to keep the two liquid phases from separating. Just how the egg-yolk can do this is a subject for later consideration; but it may be mentioned here that a stable combination of two colloidally dispersed liquids is called an *emulsion*. The whole technique of emulsions and their preparation is a most important branch of colloid chemistry, for the cosmetic, food, petroleum, and pharmaceutical industries use it constantly.

If to a little water we add a few drops of any kind of oil, we notice immediately that the oil divides itself into numerous droplets and refuses to blend with the water. As the reason for this behavior is rather complex, it will be left for later discussion. It is obvious, however, that the water is the continuous phase and the oil the dispersed phase. Now if we keep adding oil to the mixture a point will be approached at which—like the red dress with white spots—it is hard to say which of the components, the water or the oil, is dispersed in the other. In other words, after sufficient oil is added the two phases are mechanically reversed.

It is true of course that systems in which the droplets are clearly visible are not colloidal; they simply represent a type of system similar to colloids existing on a different size level. But they can be prepared as true. colloidal dispersions with the aid of a third substance called a stabilizer, not only in the laboratory but on full commercial scale. Besides mayonnaise, such preparations appear on the market in the form of the much despised fish-oil emulsions, hairwash preparations, shoe polishes, liquid waxes, and numerous other products.

The only possible phase combination in which colloidal systems do *not* exist is that of a gas dispersed in a gas. The reason for this is clear: gases are made up of molecules which are so widely separated in space that there is no possibility of enough of them getting together to form a particle of colloidal dimensions. If we take pure oxygen and add some nitrogen to it, the two gases will form a homogeneous *mixture;* but scientists do not regard such a gaseous mixture even as a true solution, because the molecules are so far apart that they cannot behave as phases—that is, they cannot interact upon each other physically in the sense that they do in liquids and solids. Physical chemists take advantage of the comparative fewness of gas molecules in a given volume to obtain much valuable information about matter that would be difficult if not impossible to discover in the liquid or solid state.

Before concluding this resumé of the types of colloidal systems, let us look at a couple of them that are somewhat more difficult to understand than the others. Under what circumstances can a liquid be colloidally dispersed in a solid? Suppose we have a small amount of oil and that we add to it a few pinches of bentonite clay, the particles of which we know are of colloidal size. This will give a clay-in-oil suspension. If more and more bentonite is put in, just as happened in the case of the oil and water, eventually the solid phase will predominate; the oil droplets will be trapped between the clay particles and a liquid-solid dispersion will result. As a matter of fact, petroleum deposits usually occur in this form; it is only on rare occasions that they are found as subterranean pools of liquid, regardless of what the prospectuses say. Petroleum is almost always tightly packed into sand or clay strata, which geologists call "oil sands." Water too is often present, and the resulting emulsions offer a tough separation problem to petroleum engineers.

Either the oil or the water may be the liquid phase in the solid, earthy continuous phase. Sometimes they are referred to in engineering parlance as "interstitial oil" or "interstitial water," which means that they are dispersed between the sand particles. Such liquid-in-solid systems may not always be of actual colloidal dimensions, but on the other hand this is entirely possible. (It must be borne in mind throughout this book that the systems mentioned frequently exist on size levels higher than the colloidal—they may be microscopic or even visible to the unaided eye; but in every case they also can and do occur as true, legitimate colloids. The parallelism of nature's structures on different levels of size has been repeatedly mentioned, and will be noted wherever it occurs as we continue.)

There is another kind of dispersion which is generally misunderstood, and for good reason. Stained glass is a colloidal system in which gold or particles of coloring matter are suspended in what certainly seems to be a solid. If this were technically true, it would have been given as an example of a solid-solid system. However, glass is considered by physical chemists to be an extremely viscous *liquid*, because it does not have the orderly crystalline structure which characterizes true solids. Its molecules have no pattern-like arrangement, but are in a condition which scientists call "random orientation." Stained glass, then, is composed of a solid dispersed phase (the coloring agent) and a technically liquid (though rigid) continuous phase.

The following table presents in brief form the possible kinds of colloidal systems, together with a few appropriate examples. Some of these systems also exist in the microscopic and ocular size ranges.

Dispersed phase	Continuous phase	Examples
1. Solid	Gas	Coal dust/air (smoke)
		Flour dust/air (in granaries)
		Pollen dust/air
		Virus/air
2. Solid	Liquid	Casein/water (milk)
		Rubber/water (latex)
		Clay/water
		Wax/water
		Starch/water
		Hemoglobin/blood serum
		Albumin/water (egg-white)
		Gold/water
		Dye/water
		Gold/glass (stained glass)
		Gelatin/water
		Soap/water
3. Solid	Solid	Carbon black/rubber
		Cement

4. Liquid	Gas	Water/air (clouds, fog)
		Water/air (sneezes)
		Antiseptic sprays
		Insecticidal sprays
5. Liquid	Liquid	Vinegar/olive oil (mayonnaise)
		Water/petroleum
		Water/fish oils
		Petroleum/water
		Cosmetic and food products
6. Liquid	Solid	Water/sand or clay
		Oil/sand or clay
		Water/paper
7. Gas	Gas	Does not occur
8. Gas	Liquid	Air/milk (whipped cream)
		Air/water (foam)
		Nitrogen/blood (emphysema)
9. Gas	Solid	Carbon dioxide/rubber (sponge rubber)
		Helium trapped in rocks as a result of radioactive decay.
		Air/rubber (sponge rubber)
		Compressed air in soap
		Air bubbles in ice

CHAPTER 4

Colloids Become Visible

○ ○

○

ALTHOUGH Thomas Graham is rightly considered to be the "father" of colloid chemistry, on the basis of his careful work and the creative thinking which lay behind it, Michael Faraday should be credited with being at least its uncle. Though his genius for experiment, observation of results, and exact deduction were primarily devoted to electrical phenomena, he nevertheless found time to be curious about other matters, one of which was the "drinkable gold" of the alchemists. He was far too critical a thinker to be satisfied with any assumptions that he could not prove. Even though he was unable to detect any particles of gold under a microscope, he was far from convinced that the golden liquids he prepared were "true" solutions. He felt rather certain that the particles were much larger than molecules. With that intuitive grasp of truth that seems to characterize all genius, he sought various ways of providing definite proof of his opinion. To understand how he hit on the idea which resulted in the first successful attempt to reveal the actual existence of colloidal particles, we shall have to attempt to reconstruct Faraday's reasoning about the problem.

An acute observer of nature by instinct, he knew that when a beam of sunlight enters a semi-dark room

through a crack in the window blind, the air so illuminated is seen to be full of dust particles. They are
made visible by the *extra* amount of light passing
through a restricted portion of the air in the room. In
this way a sufficiently strong contrast between the
lighter and darker areas is provided. As the dust is in
constant motion, the particles reveal their presence
plainly. In turning end over end or revolving in the
air, they present their various irregularly shaped surfaces to the light beam and thus appear to "twinkle"
as the angle of reflection constantly changes. The same
effect is seen in the familiar cone of light in a movie
theater.

Faraday proceeded to apply this observation to his
study of gold dispersions. Why not try illuminating a
portion of one of them with a strong beam of light? If
the particles of gold are much larger than molecules it
is possible that they may reflect or "scatter" enough
light so that their existence can at least be ascertained,
even though the individual particles themselves remain
invisible. Like the dust in the ray of light, they should
show up as a result of the contrast between the lighter
and darker parts of the solution. The results bore out
the truth of this fine piece of logical thinking. When
Faraday passed a beam of focussed light through a
preparation of colloidal gold, it cut a visible whitish
path, whereas no such path was seen when the light
beam was tried on pure water or on a true solution like
sugar and water.

This experiment proved two highly significant facts:
(1) that solid matter does exist in a very finely subdivided condition, with particles ranging between the

microscopic and the molecular size levels; and (2) that
the presence of these particles can actually be revealed
by passing a strong beam of light through the dispersion, because of scattering or reflection of the light
by the particles. Of course, this effect is obtained only
when there is a very large number of suspended particles, so that their collective reflection of the light appears as a luminous path through the liquid. If there
are comparatively few particles present, no reflection is
detectable. In the case of the darkened room or the
movie theater, the larger specks of dust can be seen
individually; but there is also a background of hazy
whiteness which indicates the presence of millions of
particles of colloidal size.

Soon after Faraday became interested in these light
experiments he was joined by another scientist, John
Tyndall, who did further work on the project. Even
today the peculiar white swath which a concentrated
light beam cuts through a colloidal solution is known
as a Tyndall cone.

Graham and Faraday were contemporaries and their
investigations were carried on at about the same time.
Faraday published his results in 1857, five years before
Graham announced that he had separated colloids from
crystalloids by dialysis through a membrane. Of the
two, Graham's researches were the more far-reaching
and specific, more painstakingly worked out. But Faraday's light test assured him the distinction of being the
first to prove conclusively the existence of the colloidal state.

It should be emphasized that both Faraday's and
Graham's work was done on systems in which the num-

ber of suspended particles per unit volume of water was extremely large—in other words, the systems were highly concentrated. The light cone just described is caused by the *total* light reflection of millions of colloidal particles. Likewise, the gooey substance which Graham found clinging to the inner side of his parchment membrane was made up of a vast number of particles *en masse*. It is one thing to prove that the colloidal state exists, but quite another to devise a means of making the individual submicroscopic particles visible.

The possibility of doing so seemed remote indeed in Graham's time. Since the simple lenses first used for actual scientific work by Anthony von Leeuwenhoek about 1700, microscopes had been gradually improved over the years. Compound microscopes, which take advantage of the greatly increased magnifying effect of two lenses, were in general use by 1860; but as knowledge of lens construction was limited, they had many defects. During the latter half of the nineteenth century the most serious of these were overcome; and by 1900 the compound microscope was able to give fairly clear resolutions of objects as small as half a micron in diameter. But this was still not sufficient to make individual colloidal particles visible.

Several investigators who had been impressed by Graham's findings were most anxious to explore the field which they saw opening out before them—provided some techniques were developed for bringing colloids under direct observation. Among them were two German optical experts, Zsigmondy and Siedentopf, the latter being director of research of the famous Zeiss

optical works in Jena. They hit on the idea of applying
the Faraday-Tyndall light effect to the compound
microscope, on the theory that if a sufficient amount of
light were directed into a rather dilute suspension, in
which the particles were relatively few and therefore
widely separated, it should be possible to distinguish
them individually under the microscope. They designed
an instrument in 1903 which has ever since been known
as the Zsigmondy-Siedentopf slit ultramicroscope—the
prefix "ultra" meaning that it makes possible the de-
tection of particles *beyond* the range of the compound
microscope. The characteristic feature of the ultramicroscope is the strong beam of focussed light with
which the specimen solution is illuminated. This light is
projected through a slit from the side, at right angles
to the barrel of the instrument. By looking through the
eyepiece, the colloidal particles appear as tiny specks
of scattered light "which hop, jump, dash together, and
fly away from each other" in a ceaseless jitterbug
dance. In this way the presence of objects far less than
one-half a micron in diameter is revealed. It is not the
particles themselves that are seen, but the impinging
light which they reflect—just as with the dust motes in
the beam of sunshine. Though we cannot see *them*, we
can see that they are there—and there is a distinct difference between those two conditions.

It is with the introduction of this ingenious device
that colloid chemistry really began, for it enabled all
types of colloidal substances to be studied directly in
the laboratory and the results to be applied to large-
scale industry. Our first accurate knowledge of the true
structure of such important materials as milk and rub-

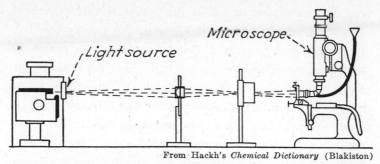

From Hackh's *Chemical Dictionary* (Blakiston)

FIG. 12   *The slit ultramicroscope—the first means of detecting the presence of colloidal particles. Its characteristic feature is a beam of light illuminating the object from the side.*

ber latex, dye dispersions, and other suspended solids was gained with the ultramicroscope; and it has served science well during the last forty years.

One of its outstanding early achievements was its irrefutable proof of the existence of molecular motion. Nearly a century before the invention of the ultramicroscope Robert Brown, an English botanist, had noticed that particles of microscopic pollen dust are in constant movement. He saw that their course did not describe any predictable path, such as a straight line or a circle, but was continually changing its direction, much like a bug darting about on the water. Brown could suggest no reason for this incessant motion, nor could other observers who studied it carefully. It was not until 1905 that a mathematical explanation was offered by Einstein—in the same year in which his theory of relativity was announced. This explanation was verified experimentally with the ultramicroscope. In a word, the so-called "Brownian motion" of a particle is caused by the impact of the *molecules* of the continuous phase, which strike the particles with sufficient force to boost them around. No sooner has the particle started moving in one direction as a result of being hit by a rapidly moving molecule than it is struck equally hard by another molecule coming from some other direction. This accounts for the darting, zigzag course which such a particle is seen to follow. Einstein and his associates were thus able to back up their mathematical facts with demonstrable proof: their theory was that the molecules of a substance are constantly moving at rather high velocities. The particles whose presence is revealed in the ultramicroscope, though of colloidal size, were sufficiently close to molecular dimensions to serve as examples. Not only are they in Brownian motion themselves, but they act *like* molecules in causing it in larger bodies. This fact is mentioned to indicate the tremendous importance of the introduction of the ultramicroscope in establishing the truth of this basic natural phenomenon. To a greater or less extent, Brownian motion is a characteristic property of such objects as fat particles in milk, rubber particles in latex, and blood cells and similar bodies suspended in liquids, and can easily be observed under a compound microscope. The velocity of the particles diminishes rapidly as their size increases.

Although studies of basic significance for the development of the science of colloid chemistry were made with the ultramicroscope—studies which led Wolfgang Ostwald to name this newly discovered range of sizes "the world of neglected dimensions"—the natural curiosity of scientists was far from assuaged. The goal had not yet been reached. How long could they be content with seeing mere flecks of light helter-skeltering around? They were far from optimistic, for they well knew that all objects were made visible by reflecting natural light, and that this light travels in waves which are only a little over half a micron "long." This "length"—which is really the distance between the crest of one light wave and the crest of the next—effectively limits the size of objects which can be resolved by any instrument which depends on natural light for its source of illumination. Particles of smaller sizes are unable to interfere with, or disturb, the light waves which fall on them, in much the same sense that the meshes of a coarse sieve cannot prevent the passage of a grain of sand. The only chance of throwing the "world of neglected dimensions" open to direct, actual observation lay in the possibility of using a form of light whose wave crests were closer together than those of sunlight—in conventional terms, a light of shorter wave length.

Serious attempts were made in this direction. A microscope was developed which utilized only ultraviolet light rays, which are considerably shorter than those of natural light. Some improvement was obtained, in that particles twice as small as any observed with the ordinary compound microscope could be detected. But this was too low a factor to be of great practical value; the need was for a fifty- or one-hundred-fold increase in resolving power, which would require a type of light whose wave length was about 50,000 times as short as that of visible light. Such rays would of course make no impression on the retina of the eye. Indeed, not even ultraviolet rays are visible. Yet the problem of seeing

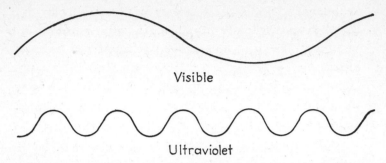

Visible

Ultraviolet

Electronic

FIG. 13   *A rough idea of long and short light waves, which produce both visible and invisible light. Ultraviolet rays are from ten to one hundred times as short as the visible waves of sunlight; electronic waves are from 50,000 to 100,000 times as short.*

colloidal particles in the exact sense of the word demanded a unique kind of illumination capable of being reflected by objects in this size range.

A solution lay at hand in the so-called cathode-ray tube which originated in the laboratories of English and German physicists late in the nineteenth century. The principle on which it operates is fairly simple. Positive and negative electrical terminals are sealed into a glass tube from which as much air as possible has been removed, giving an almost complete vacuum. An electric current is then applied. This causes electrons to be torn from the metallic surface of the negative terminal, or cathode, and to hurtle through the vacuum to the opposite end of the tube. Such devices are popularly called vacuum tubes, and in the last twenty years they have become the basis of all varieties of electronic equipment. It was with a variant of this tube that Roentgen accidentally discovered x-rays in 1895.

X-rays are still another kind of light, the waves of which are much shorter than ultraviolet—enough shorter indeed to meet the requirements for resolving colloidal particles. Unfortunately they are not adaptable to use in a microscope. Even though today they are a valuable adjunct to the scientists' equipment for studying matter, they permit one to ascertain only its crystal structure, just as they enable a physician to see the human skeleton, which obviously is very different from a real flesh-and-blood photograph. Useful as Roentgen's discovery was for both science and medicine, it was merely incidental to the development of an improved microscope.

To condense the investigations of thirty years into a few sentences, extensive work with the cathode-ray or vacuum tube revealed three important facts: (1) The stream of electrons passing through it was found to be deflected from a straight line by bringing a magnet close to the outside of the tube. The field of force created by the magnet is sufficient to pull the electrons around in a semi-circular path. (2) The electrons give off, or are accompanied by, light waves which are even shorter than x-rays, and may be fully 50,000 times as short as waves of natural light if sufficient voltage is used. (3) The shape of an object placed between the cathode, which is the source of the electrons, and a light-sensitive screen at the opposite end of the tube appears distinctly outlined and enlarged upon the screen. This remarkable fact indicates beyond doubt that the object blocks off the electron rays and thus

Fig. 14   *Shadow of a metal obstacle cast
by the electron stream in a cathode tube.*

projects its image on the fluorescent screen; the size of
the image is governed by the position of the object
relative to the cathode.

These three phenomena combined to make possible
the development of one of the marvels of modern science
—the so-called electron microscope. The names of several pioneer workers in both Germany and America are
memorable for this splendid piece of electronic research. In 1926 Hans Busch thought of utilizing the
magnetic deflection property of electrons to *focus* the
ultra-short light waves emanating from the electron
stream. He realized that no use could ever be made of
this newly discovered light source unless some agency
were found to perform the function of the glass lenses
in an ordinary microscope. Experimenting with the behavior of electrons as they pass through magnetic
fields, he eventually proved that they can be so deflected as to focus the electron beam and thus to give a
greatly magnified image. At this point, Max Knoll and
Ernst Ruska took over the problem of applying this
principle to the actual construction of an electron

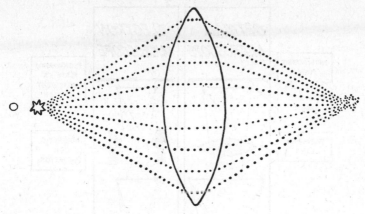

FIG. 15 *How a convex glass lens bends light rays. Light changes its direction in passing from air into glass and then from glass into air.*

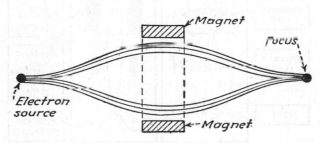

FIG. 16 *How electron light rays are focussed by passing through a magnetic field.*

microscope. Their first crude model was built in 1932. Though defective in many respects, it proved that the extremely short light waves present in an electronic vacuum tube can be focussed by passing them through a series of magnetic lenses, and that objects well down in the range of colloidal sizes can be resolved quite clearly. Ladislaus Marton in Belgium and Reinhold Rudenberg in Germany also were active in these early

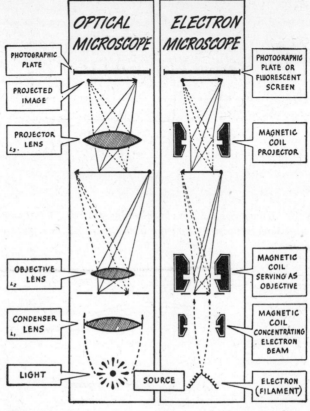

FIG. 17 *Comparison of optical and electron micro-scopes.*

developments. However, none of the European scientists succeeded in obtaining a completely successful instrument. In Toronto, Professor E. F. Burton and his associates, James Hillier and Albert Prebus, constructed the first electron microscope in America, with which they obtained conclusive evidence as to the exact particle shape of carbon black in 1941. V. K. Zworykin and his associates of the Radio Corporation of

America began commercial manufacture of electron microscopes in 1942. Since then, new and improved models have followed each other rapidly, and today there are hundreds of these elaborate instruments in research laboratories all over the United States and Canada (see Plate VI).

Just what does the electron microscope accomplish and how is it useful to industry and biology? By far the most valuable asset of the new instrument is its almost uncanny acuteness of vision. It was mentioned in an earlier chapter that microscopists call this "resolving power." As might be expected, the higher the resolving power, the more useful the microscope. By virtue of the extremely short light waves used, the electron microscope is most exceptionally endowed in this respect: it can clearly distinguish particles and dimensions of colloidal size and give them astonishing magnifications.

Solid objects are best suited to its capabilities—particles such as carbon black, colloidal metals, clays, and the like. As these are extremely dense they completely block off the electrons. Consequently their shape is reproduced on the fluorescent screen or on the photographic plate, which is usually employed to make pictures such as those shown here. The jagged particles of mine dust (Plate VII) and pollen dust (Plate VIII), both magnified thousands of times, indicate the amazing power of the electron microscope. The jagged edges on the mine dust fragments are of true colloidal dimensions; they could not be seen at all in an ordinary microscope. In the case of the pollen dust, the protuberances on the surface are also good examples of what is meant by colloidal roughness; only the high resolving power of the electron microscope makes them visible. Such surface irregularity has an important bearing on the catalytic properties of metallic powders, to be discussed later. When one stops to consider that such objects were completely beyond the range of any microscope up to a few years ago, the true significance of this instrument becomes apparent. In the realm of solid objects it has taught research chemists a great deal about paint pigments, food products, latex particles in rubber, dyes and their dispersions, the structure of textile and paper fibers, the surface appearance and particle shape of all manner of earthy and metallic materials, the complex nature of cement—indeed, there is scarcely an industry of any importance in which the revelations of the electron microscope have not already been of vast technical value.

By means of a complicated replica process the apparently flat surfaces of metal sheets have been brought within its scope. Here ridges and furrows appear like miniature mountain ranges and overlapping rock ledges on specimens of machined and polished aluminum or steel. Such discoveries are of great importance for the metallurgical industries, especially in the manufacture of aircraft pistons and other precision parts which operate at high speeds at minute clearances. The replica technique, which involves taking a plastic impression of the specimen surface for direct examination in the electron microscope, has been applied to substances other than metals. It is perhaps the most significant advance in the methods of specimen preparation since the instrument was introduced.

Important as the electron microscope has proved to

be for industrial purposes, perhaps its greatest contribution to human welfare will be in the biological and medical sciences. Just as improved optical microscopes led the way to successful attacks on diseases which were rampant generations ago, so this new super-microscope may aid in abolishing such scourges as influenza, poliomyelitis, and other types of virus infections. Not only can ordinary bacteria like those of pneumonia and typhoid be studied at close range—their structure observed and the means by which they thrive or die under the influence of drugs or bacteriophages photographed —but the much smaller virus bodies themselves can be isolated. Bacteria belong to what we have designated as the microscopic range of sizes, whereas viruses are of colloidal dimensions. So tiny are they in fact that even with the electron microscope the utmost skill and care are required to identify them. Since they pass through ordinary filters, which remove bacteria, they are generally known as filtrable viruses. Much of the credit for this work belongs to Drs. Stuart Mudd, Wendell M. Stanley, and Thomas A. Anderson, who are in the forefront of medical research with the electron microscope.

Bacteria are micro-organisms consisting of single cells. Like the cells of all living tissue they contain centrally located structures which are much denser than the colloidal protoplasm which envelopes them, and are themselves enclosed in protective coatings. An electron micrograph, to be useful, depends on the extent to which the electrons penetrate the less dense, almost transparent protoplasm, thus projecting an image of the internal structure of the cell on the photographic plate. Unfortunately the ability of electrons to pass through matter in large enough numbers to produce the required result is very limited, because their direction is abruptly changed whenever they strike the slightest obstacle. The effect is much the same sort of "scattering" we have already referred to in the case of the ultramicroscope. As a result of this low penetrating power, considerable difficulty was encountered in obtaining good pictures of cells and tissues. The staining technique which proved so useful with the optical microscope can be used effectively to counteract this defect; it intensifies the density of the internal structures so that they stand out clearly (Plate XXI).

Bacteria and viruses are made up of protein complexes. Certain types of plant virus, such as the tobacco mosaic (Plate XX) are considered to be among the simplest forms of life. They lie on the hazy borderline which divides the animate from the inanimate. The omnipresence of proteins in all living tissue makes them one of the most important groups of compounds in the entire range of chemistry. They are essential to health and growth, are rich in energy, and a vital necessity for the continuance of life on earth. Some authorities believe that the origin of life may be traced to the first protein molecule formed—by what process we have no means of knowing.

Special mention of proteins is made here not only because of their vast importance to biology and medicine, but because they comprise a special group of colloidal aggregates called macromolecules which are clearly visible in the electron microscope. It so happens that proteins are highly complicated substances, the molecules of which are extremely large. Composed basically of the elements carbon, oxygen, hydrogen, and nitrogen, and usually sulphur as well, the simple forms are of normal molecular dimensions. One of their characteristics, however, is that they seldom appear stripped down to their basic form; rather, they tend to join together in extensive interwoven chain- and netlike structures. Such reticulated combinations are so large that they behave like colloidal particles, and are well within this size range. Technically they are still molecules, because to subdivide one of them would destroy that particular substance; yet they are just as truly colloids as any other objects of equal dimensions. This fact again bears out the statement that colloid chemistry is concerned far more with size and shape than with chemical composition.

Most of the organic substances with which we are concerned in this book are proteins of one kind or another. They occur in bacteria, in plants, in milk, in eggs, in blood, in tissue—virtually everywhere that biologists look with their recently acquired aid, the electron microscope. It may be that some of the most profound secrets of life lie in this direction. Certainly a tremendous amount of research on the part of our most capable physical chemists has been devoted to them in recent years. As a group, proteins and their behavior are actually becoming a separate department of science called *biophysics*—a name which is still little used, but which is likely to grow rapidly in acceptance. This entire subject of proteins and their relation to life will be discussed in detail in Chapter 13.

It is true, then, that large molecules can be detected in the electron microscope. None the less, average molecules like those of water, sugar, or salt are far beyond its range. Obviously, atoms are still more so. It is possible that with improvement in the mechanical efficiency of magnetic lenses—which are remarkably poor in performance when the resolution they actually give is compared with that of which they are theoretically capable —it may be possible to distinguish particles below the colloidal size range. For the present, however, there are plenty of problems to be studied within it.

CHAPTER 5

Electrical Lifebelts

I<small>T IS NOW</small> high time to distinguish between two broad classes of colloidal particles. The eight different kinds of systems already described represent a sort of horizontal classification, as it were, based on the physical state of the continuous and dispersed phases—that is, whether they are solid, liquid, or gaseous. The line of cleavage now referred to is a vertical one, which separates one *kind* of colloid particle from another. There are borderline cases, of course, in which the two kinds are combined or in which the dividing line is hazy; but in general the distinction is a valid one. It was hinted at in the discussion of Thomas Graham's experiments; indeed, Graham was the first to recognize it and to suggest the words to express it.

If a colloidal dispersion was in the form of a liquid, such as particles of gold or bentonite clay in water, in which the particles are hard and dense, he called the system a "sol," which is merely a convenient shortening of "solution." In general, the particles of a "sol" tend to repel the surrounding water rather strongly. Once this type of suspension is destroyed, it can never be reconstituted; it is said to be "irreversible." If, however, a system contained a soft, sticky material as the dispersed phase, and changed from a thick liquid to a firm, viscous mass when cool, Graham termed it a "gel," which obviously suggests the familiar word "gelatin." Examples of this kind of colloid are water dispersions of glue, starch, egg white, pectin, and of course gelatin. The characteristic properties of the "gel" group are quite opposite to those of the "sols." The particles have a strong attraction for water; moreover, after most of the water has evaporated and the system has set to a stiff paste, in most cases it can be restored to its original condition by adding water. Such systems are therefore called "reversible gels."

This distinction is based on something more than the physical state of the dispersions, even though Graham probably did not suspect it at the time he christened them. It can best be understood by answering the question, "Why is it that colloidal particles do not settle out; what force is present to offset the pull of gravity upon them?" The fact is that the two types of colloidal particles just distinguished are held in suspension by two quite different phenomena which are closely related to the fact that solid particles repel water whereas soft, sticky ones attract it. This basic difference underlies Graham's classification of "sol" and "gel." For the present, let us bid the "gels" farewell, and become acquainted with the highly important properties of their brethren, the "sols."

The friction created by a moving body against the surrounding substance tends to build up a charge of static electricity on its surface. Examples of this are generally familiar in daily experience: rubbing a glass rod with fur, passing a comb swiftly through the hair, or a stream of water flowing through a pipe. The accumulated charge, which may be either positive or negative, is due to the transference of electrons from one body to the other; the one that loses them becomes positively charged, and vice-versa. It is simple enough to prove that this charge is bona fide electrical energy by bringing a good conductor close to the charged object. A spark will fly, with a slight crackling sound, and if the discharging agent is your finger, you will receive a very slight shock. Everyone has seen the chains dangling from the rear of gasoline trucks; these are for the purpose of safely carrying off the static generated by the friction of the fuel as it slops around inside the tank. A similar function is performed by the metal "brushes" sometimes seen at automobile toll gates. A car accumulates a slight surface charge as it moves rapidly against the air, and this would be discharged into the body of the toll collector if it were not previously grounded by the tall brush which the car must pass over as it enters the toll station. The shock would be negligible if only one car an hour went through; but when a collector is touching cars at the rate of fifty or sixty an hour, his system could be appreciably affected if the charge were not removed.

If anyone doubts that these surface electrical charges exert a measurable force, let him try to pick up a piece of typewriter copy paper from the top of a table on a sultry day. He will be aware of a distinct attraction between the paper and the table, indicating that electrical forces of opposite charge exist between them. When the sheet is removed from the table its free end will tend to fly about and be generally unmanageable until the surface charge is lost to a conducting substance. Likewise, sheets of paper going through printing presses sometimes accumulate such high static charges from the friction of the rollers that it would be difficult to handle them at the take-off end if a special neutralizing device were not used.

The rule that objects carrying similar electrical charges—that is, both positive or both negative—repel each other and that those bearing unlike charges attract each other is familiar to everyone. This is the principle used in the neutralizing method just referred to; and it is profoundly important in colloid chemistry. The reason why the sheets of paper are unmanageable is that they all are strongly charged with positive electricity, and therefore are mutually repellant when brought close together. As a result they "fight" each other, refuse to lie flat, and curl at the edges. The obvious remedy is to provide a source of *negative* electricity at the point where they feed out of the press. The negative charges are at once drawn to the positive ones on the surface of the paper and promptly cancel them—and the sheets lie down meekly in their rack.

To return to the questions we are trying to answer, we recall that a typical solid-in-liquid colloidal system consists of a finely divided material like bentonite clay or gold, suspended in water. We know also that these particles will not settle to the bottom of the container after long standing, and that they are in constant rapid motion, caused by impact of the molecules of water. Adhering tightly to the surface of each particle is a respectable charge of negative electricity, the effect of which is to insulate or repel it from its neighbors and thus to prevent it from undergoing innumerable col-

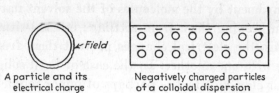

A particle and its
electrical charge

Negatively charged particles
of a colloidal dispersion

FIG. 18   *At left is an attempt to represent a particle surrounded by a field of electrical force. This field constitutes a "charge," which may be either positive or negative. The right-hand picture suggests a colloidal dispersion of negatively charged particles; the charge is conventionally indicated by a minus sign.*

lisions. In diagrams such as Figure 18, as well as in chemical notation, the charge is usually indicated by a plus or a minus sign, depending on whether it is positive or negative, placed above or to the right of the symbol; the charge is actually a sort of force envelope, or "field," surrounding each particle and protecting it from too close approach to its neighbors. Though the situation is actually somewhat more complicated than shown here, a certain amount of oversimplification is inevitable.

These charges have several important consequences. In the first place, they are the agency which prevents the dispersion from settling out of solution; since the particles are so tiny, the pull of gravity on each one is so extremely slight that it is outbalanced by the force of the electrical charges, which may be compared to lifebelts. The instant a particle tries to sink, it encounters the similarly charged field of the particle below. It is at once repelled, and so cannot fall farther. The ceaseless Brownian motion of the particles due to bombardment by the molecules of the solvent naturally aids in keeping them from settling; but notwithstanding this, the electrical charges prevent them from colliding with one another. In the case of hard solids like gold or clay, this fact is perhaps of minor importance; but in suspensions like milk and rubber latex, in which the surfaces of the particles are rather soft and sticky, it is highly significant, for if it were not for the electrical repulsion the particles would strike one another as they go cavorting about, and cohere into a solid mass. Another significant fact is that the force area around the particle serves to insulate it from the surrounding water. For this reason materials having external electrical charges are said to be "hydrophobic," or water-hating.

As a result of the existence of these surface charges, several important industrial applications have been developed. In fact most of the means by which electrically stabilized colloids are controlled and used by man are made possible by their presence. They provide an unfailing method of moving the particles in predetermined directions and of destroying the dispersion altogether at an instant's notice. For example, suppose that two metallic electrodes, A and B, are placed in a container of "drinkable gold." One of them is the positive terminal, or *anode* (A^+), the other the negative terminal, or *cathode* (B^-), as shown in Figure 19. Each particle of gold wears its life-preserver of negative charge (only the charges are indicated in the diagram). As soon as the current starts to flow between the two terminals, all the particles will move toward the anode (A^+), in obedience to the universal law of attraction of

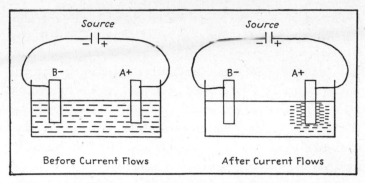

FIG. 19 *Migration of charged particles under the influence of a direct electric current. The particles, represented by minus signs, are uniformly distributed in the solution when no current is passing; when it is turned on, they move to the oppositely charged terminal and either adhere to it (latex) or fall to the bottom of the container (solids).*

oppositely charged bodies. When they touch it, the negative charge on the particle and the positive charge on the anode will neutralize each other, and the experiment will end with a gold-plated anode, because of the natural affinity of the gold for the metal electrode. If the same treatment is accorded to a suspension of clay particles, they also travel to the anode. There the opposing charges cancel each other and the particles, divested of their lifebelts, fall to the bottom of the container.

In general, any migration of colloidal particles induced by an electrical current is known as *electrophoresis*. When the substance is of such a nature that it will form a coating on the electrode, the process is called *electrodeposition*. It is quite possible to observe this in the ultramicroscope. In the range of atomic sizes the same phenomenon occurs, in which charged atoms of various metals are plated onto electrodes of various shapes and sizes; this is termed *electrolysis*.

For some purposes colloidal dispersions are desirable, but for others they are not only undesirable but actually harmful. Fortunately, effective means have been found whereby the unwanted ones can be destroyed and the beneficial ones maintained. The balance of this chapter will be devoted to describing briefly several industrial applications of colloid chemistry in which the suspensions are destroyed. In each case the destruction is accomplished by the electrical precipitation method described above. It can be applied to both solid-in-gas and solid-in-liquid systems.

The presence of colloidally suspended solids in the air in heavily industrialized areas can be a serious menace to the health of the community, as well as an unmitigated nuisance from the point of view of cleanliness and comfort. Interesting figures have been published from time to time on the "dirtiness" of the atmosphere in our leading cities. For many years the unenviable position of the nation's most begrimed city was Pittsburgh, but it has recently yielded this distinction to St. Louis; and some other large cities have nothing to boast about in this respect.

One of the most offensive solid materials in the air is soft coal soot and smoke. Other miscellaneous dusts due to factory operations in cement, chemical, and pigment manufacturing areas contribute to the problem. Some of these smoke and dust particles are large enough to fall of their own accord after being released to the air, but the most dangerous ones are those which remain suspended in the air indefinitely because of the stabilizing effect of their electrical charges. Would it not be possible, in the very worst cases at least, to build some sort of precipitating device into stacks and flues so that most of the colloidal particles could be removed before the smoke was released? In 1883 Sir Oliver Lodge in England had been unsuccessful in an attempt to do so. Later an American scientist, Dr. Frederick G. Cottrell, decided to do further work on the problem.

He invented a simple mechanism for this purpose which has since become known as the Cottrell precipitator and has been installed in countless locations where dust abatement became a critical problem. A metal vent flue about fifteen feet high, which the dust-laden air enters at the bottom, is positively charged with 50,000 volts or more of direct current by a wire which passes vertically through it. As the negatively charged particles travel upward through the flue they are attracted to the wall and neutralized. The metal wall acts like one of the electrodes shown in Figure 19, and the wire like the other. The supporting charges thus being removed from the particles, they fall to a collector box at the bottom of the flue. If a very large volume of gas is to be handled, a battery of several flues is necessary. This effective and inexpensive device has greatly reduced air contamination in large cities. A household model called the Precipitron has recently been perfected by the Westinghouse Electric and Manufacturing Company. It substitutes horizontal charged plates for the walls of the flue. These developments well illustrate the practical value of understanding the behavior of colloidal particles.

Although smokes in general are properly considered

to be colloidal in nature, there are certain artificial types intended for military use which are specifically designed to settle rapidly. Everyone is familiar with the smoke screen ejected from airplanes, which drops like a curtain of dazzling whiteness. The reason for this is that the chief ingredient of the mixture is a heavy pigment known as titanium dioxide, to which the whiteness is due. Though the particles are of colloidal dimensions their specific gravity is purposely made high by the titanium dioxide, so that the normal stabilizing effect of the electrical charges will not interfere with their rapid descent. World War II gave a tremendous boost to artificial smoke research for purposes of concealment and camouflage. The Chemical Warfare Service reports that a smoke generator was perfected by the time American troops landed in North Africa capable of blanketing an area of one square mile with an impenetrable smoke in about ten minutes. Its mechanism has not been disclosed.

A condition still more serious than smoke and dust contamination exists in flour mills, where the air becomes so laden with charged particles that damaging explosions or fires may occur. Those whose memory for such things is good may recall such a catastrophe in Port Arthur, Manitoba, in September of 1945. The accumulation of static electrical energy in the air creates a condition in which the slightest spark from a pipe or from one metal object striking another is very likely to touch off an explosive discharge or a raging fire. This too can be remedied by feeding electricity of opposite charge into the system; robbed of their sustaining force, the flour particles drop out of the air, and all threat of fire and danger to the health of workers is removed. This system is also applicable to coal mines and other special cases in which a high proportion of colloidal dusts is present.

Fogs and mists can also be dispelled in this manner on a relatively small scale. The Cottrell precipitation process has been successfully applied to the vapors arising from sulfuric acid and other chemical manufacturing plants. This suggests interesting possibilities for future installations on air fields and at other critical points. As a matter of fact, a considerable degree of control over fogs has been achieved on an experimental scale by a unique method involving sound vibrations which are far above the range of the human ear, known as *ultrasonic* waves. Fogs can be artificially created in small containers of common liquids like water or benzene by passing through them these high-intensity sound waves by means of an elaborate transmitting mechanism. The space above the liquid in the container is quickly filled with a thick cloud of atomized liquid particles. The reverse effect—the precipitation of colloidal droplets from a gaseous medium—is also possible. By exposing a fog to the action of ultrasonic waves, the frequency of collision of the particles is so greatly increased that they tend to collect into aggregates, which soon become so large that they overcome the sustaining force of their electrical charges. All this of course is still in the laboratory stage; yet it is not impossible that ways will be found to apply it to one of the most persistent and formidable enemies of aviation —ceiling zero.

An attack on the fog problem from a new angle was

recently announced by the prolific General Electric Research Laboratories. Dr. Vincent J. Schaefer succeeded in turning a "cloud" of supercooled water droplets first into ice crystals and then into snow inside an ordinary deep-freeze unit by dropping a pinch of solid carbon dioxide into it; he subsequently accomplished this in the grand manner by flying a plane through a real cloud at below freezing temperature, scattering a few pounds of the same substance behind him en route. This is an interesting phenomenon from the colloidal point of view. The water droplets, which exist in liquid form at $-25°F$, far below the freezing point—in a supercooled condition, as physicists say—apparently condense on colloidal ice nuclei which are formed by the carbon dioxide. Being far colder than the fog particles $(-80°F)$, it is able to convert those few bits of moisture which are in its immediate neighborhood into ice crystals, since water cannot remain supercooled below about $-30°F$, but freezes spontaneously. Once these few nuclei, about a micron in diameter, are created locally by the tremendous cold of the carbon dioxide, they serve as cores upon which the remaining fog particles precipitate. As a result, large ice crystals build up and fall in the form of snow when they reach sufficient size. This technique has obvious possibilities in preventing ice-formation on airplanes and dissipating fogs over cities and airports in winter. Here it might be said that the carbon dioxide acts as a catalyst.

Another industrial technique of some importance which involves the attraction of colloidal particles to an oppositely charged electrode is the so-called "anode process" used in the manufacture of thin rubber goods of high quality but of irregular shape, such as surgeon's gloves and miscellaneous drug sundries. It has proved superior in both excellence of product and cheapness of operation to the conventional method of molding in a hydraulic press. In other cases, this method makes possible the manufacture of rubber-coated wire mesh, screening, and similar articles which could not be made at all in the ordinary way.

Two electrodes—anode and cathode—are placed in a bath of suitably compounded rubber latex. The anode, or positively charged electrode, has the shape of the article to be made. When the current is allowed to pass through the system, the negatively charged latex particles migrate to the anode and deposit themselves upon it. As long as the current flow is maintained the migration continues, until the desired result is obtained. A coating of any thickness up to as much as a quarter of an inch is possible. It is necessary of course to see that there is enough latex available to produce a complete article. If the supply runs low it can be replenished. Each particle of rubber in the latex, attracted by the positively charged anode, moves toward it, gives up its charge, and clings to the metal form, which is usually zinc or zinc-coated steel. One layer coheres to another because of the strong tendency of unvulcanized rubber to stick to itself and to most metals. When the accumulated layer is thick enough, the current is shut off and the form withdrawn. The rubber deposit, to which the necessary vulcanizing ingredients have previously been added, is then stripped off and "cured," except when the anode itself is part of the finished product, as in rubber-insulated screening. This method is an excellent example of electrodeposition of a colloidal substance; it gives a more uniform product that can be obtained in other ways. Many factors must be closely controlled to insure success, and a great deal of careful experimentation was necessary to establish correct conditions for large-scale production.

A succeeding chapter will deal in more detail with rubber latex, which is one of the most interesting and important of the industrial colloids. The instances described here, however, are designed merely to show how responsive colloidal systems are to the influence of an electric current or field, and how usefully this property can be applied to matters of importance in problems of daily life.

In this and later chapters no attempt will be made to present an exhaustive treatment of the manifold applications of colloid chemistry. The main lines along which knowledge has advanced will be indicated and appropriate examples will be given of each. So wide is the field and so many the individual cases—each with its own specific set of peculiarities and problems of control— that it would require a dozen volumes of this size even to summarize them. Now that we have become acquainted with the possibilities presented by electrical charges in colloidal systems, it may be asked whether or not this always necessitates the use of an external source of electricity, as in the Cottrell and anode processes. Because the answer to this highly important question involves a little explanation, especially for those whose chemistry is rusty, we had better start a fresh chapter.

CHAPTER 6

The Purification of Water

○ ○

○

So CLOSELY are the physical sciences interrelated that it is virtually impossible to single out one of them for discussion without involving several of the others. Indeed it is neither practicable nor desirable to attempt to divide them into compartments; they must be considered as parts of a unified, closely knit whole if one is to understand the truly marvelous organization which makes up the physical universe. Colloid chemistry merges imperceptibly into several other sciences: physics, physiology, electrochemistry, and chemistry. It is to the last of these that we shall now be obliged to turn for a moment (the preceding chapters have touched upon electrochemistry). This is done to make clear one of the most practical methods for getting rid of colloidal suspensions in cases where they are highly undesirable.

It is common knowledge that salty water freezes considerably below 32°F. No ice forms on harbors and coastal inlets except after an unusually long period of zero weather. The addition of a fistfull of rock salt to the cracked ice in an ice cream freezer will keep the water liquid at a temperature far below the freezing point; in fact it is possible to lower the temperature of water to −60° or −70°F in this way. Perhaps it is not so generally known that the boiling point of water can be noticeably raised by the same means. On the other hand, if the *same proportion* of sugar is dissolved in pure water, the freezing point is again reduced and the boiling point increased, but *to a much less marked extent.* Evidently there is a basic difference between the action of salt and sugar when they are in solution.

To begin with, why should there be any effect at all? Presumably because the freezing and boiling points of a liquid are closely related to its molecular structure. When a foreign substance like sugar is added, its molecules, or particles, at once form a "true solution." The sudden appearance in the water of a large number of molecules of another substance influences its reaction to temperature changes, with the result that its freezing point is lowered and its boiling point raised. The extent of this effect is directly proportional to the concentration of the solution: the more sugar dissolved, the greater the change. The simplest form of the sugar molecule, which is rather large compared with a water molecule, is $C_6H_{12}O_6$. This combination of twenty-four atoms remains welded together as a unit, and undergoes no further simplification in solution.

But look what happens to the salt molecule—the well-known sodium chloride ($NaCl$), comprised of only two atoms. No sooner is salt mixed with water than each of its molecules splits into two parts. Though the total number of added molecules of $NaCl$ and $C_6H_{12}O_6$ may be identical *before* they are placed in the water, the number of salt particles suddenly *doubles* as the salt goes into solution. This sharp increase in the number of particles accounts for the marked effect of salt on the freezing and boiling points of water—much greater than that caused by sugar because the concentration of dissolved particles is automatically doubled. This phenomenon is called *ionization;* the two fragments of the salt molecule were christened *ions* because of their characteristic of rapid movement.

However, this is only half the story. When the sodium chloride molecule divides, it does not become simply one atom of sodium and one of chlorine. The chemical union of these atoms was originally accomplished by the mutual sharing of an electron originally belonging to the sodium atom only; but when the split takes place, the electron in question is shorn away from the sodium atom and becomes the exclusive property of the chlorine. Since in their original uncombined state both atoms were electrically neutral, the result of this appropriation by chlorine of one electron originally belonging to sodium is to give the chlorine atom an *extra* electron and to leave the sodium atom short an electron. Since an electron is visualized as having a single negative charge, it is evident that the sodium ion now has one too many positive charges and the chloride ion one too few. In a word, ionization impairs the electrical balance of the atoms of a compound; when they separate in solution one of them becomes positively charged by loss of an electron and the other becomes negatively charged by gaining an electron. Chemists usually indicate this situation by placing plus and minus signs beside the symbols of ionized compounds: thus each molecule of salt ($NaCl$) added to water becomes two ions, one of which is sodium (Na⁺) and the other chloride (Cl⁻).

Some compounds ionize in solution and others do not. The latter are for the most part compounds containing carbon. We shall be chiefly concerned with those that do so, as their effects on colloidal systems are profound and highly useful. Before going further, it may be noted that some substances yield ions which have two or even three electrical charges. For example, sulphuric acid (H_2SO_4) gives two single-charged hydrogen ions (H^+) and one double-charged sulphate ion (SO_4^{--}); and aluminum sulfate [$Al_2(SO_4)_3$] produces two triple-charged aluminum ions (Al^{+++}) and three double-charged sulphate ions (SO_4^{--}). All acids ionize readily, and as every acid contains the element hydrogen, addition of acid to a solution always causes the appearance of a large contingent of hydrogen ions. For this reason the hydrogen ion concentration of a solution is taken as an index of its acidity. The ions formed from compounds like salt, which have only one electrical charge, are called *monovalent;* those having two charges are *divalent;* and those with three, *trivalent.* Substances that ionize in solution are collectively known as *electrolytes,* because by dividing into two oppositely charged ions they increase the electrical conductivity of the water or other solvent. Water containing salt or sulphuric acid is a much better transmitter of electricity than pure water.

At this point a list of the most commonly used electrolytes, showing their ions and charges, may be helpful in summarizing the foregoing description.

Name	Formula	Positive ion	Negative ion
Sodium chloride (salt)	NaCl	1 Na$^+$	1 Cl$^-$
Hydrochloric acid	HCl	1 H$^+$	1 Cl$^-$
Sulphuric acid	H$_2$SO$_4$	2 H$^+$	1 (SO$_4$)$^{--}$
Aluminum sulphate	Al$_2$(SO$_4$)$_3$	2 Al^{+++}	3 (SO$_4$)$^{--}$
Magnesium chloride	MgCl$_2$	1 Mg^{++}	2 Cl$^-$
Sodium hydroxide (caustic soda)	NaOH	1 Na$^+$	1 (OH)$^-$
Sodium carbonate	Na$_2$CO$_3$	2 Na$^+$	1 (CO$_3$)$^{--}$
Calcium chloride	CaCl$_2$	1 Ca^{++}	2 Cl$^-$
Potassium nitrate	KNO$_3$	1 K$^+$	1 (NO$_3$)$^-$
Ferric chloride	FeCl$_3$	1 Fe^{+++}	3 Cl$^-$

The practical bearing of this rather complex subject of ions upon colloid chemistry must now be obvious. The addition of an electrolyte to a solid-liquid system, for example, achieves much the same result as passing an electric current through it. In a suspension of negatively charged gold particles, a pinch of salt or a drop or two of hydrochloric acid at once provides enough positive ions (which belong to the *atomic* size range) to neutralize them; as a result, the gold particles fall to the bottom of the container. Once more their electrical lifebelts are removed by opposing electrical charges.* This process is variously called precipitation, coagulation, and clarification, depending on the nature of the particles and the way in which their removal occurs.

* It should, perhaps be pointed out that the entire picture here is more complicated than can be described clearly within the limited confines of this book. Actually, compensating positive ions surround the gold particles in the original colloidal solution and these ions are exchanged against positive ions of the hydrochloric acid or salt which is introduced as a precipitant. It is the higher affinity of the positive ions introduced into the colloidal solution which compels them to unite with gold particles.

The electrical potential on colloidal particles, which we have likened to a life preserver, varies with the nature and size of the particle; but it is a definitely measurable force which, as has been pointed out, repels electrical charges of the same kind and attracts those of the opposite kind. Suppose we imagine a negatively charged gold particle surrounded by its field of force, or lifebelt. What happens as positively charged ions enter the system? The charge on the gold particle will decrease, because a portion of it is neutralized by the ions of the electrolyte. As just indicated, the ions of various substances differ greatly in their neutralizing power, the trivalent aluminum ion being much more powerful than the monovalent hydrogen ion. Therefore a very little aluminum sulphate added to the gold solution would be as effective as a much larger quantity of hydrochloric acid.

To go on with our gold particle, it is obvious that as more and more electrolyte is added, the negative potential on the particle will continue to decrease gradually; it will approach and finally reach the value of zero—at which time precipitation or coagulation will occur. The so-called "lifebelt" charge can be visualized as being eaten away by added ions of opposite charge until it is finally consumed completely; in other words, the electrical potential is reduced progressively until it disappears. When this happens, the particle is said to have reached its *isoelectric point*. This is a most important property of any colloidal system, for it is here that its future existence hangs in the balance. Substances vary in the amount and kind of electrolyte required to attain their isoelectric points, and the acidity or alkalinity of the surrounding liquid is also a related factor.

With the principle of positively and negatively charged ions clearly in mind, we are in a position to understand many interesting and highly important applications of colloid chemistry to the seemingly commonplace facts of ordinary life. In the first chapter, the purification of municipal water supplies by sand filtration was mentioned, with the proviso that the subject would be resumed. As a starter, then, a glance at the solution of this difficulty is in order.

As it comes from rivers, streams, and lakes, water is likely to be more or less contaminated with impurities. Their nature and extent vary greatly with the locality, of course, but even under better than average conditions the contamination is considerable. We are not referring here to the presence of dissolved compounds of calcium and magnesium due to the geological structure of the terrain through which the water flows. These cause the so-called "hardness" which is generally familiar; but as these substances exist in the water as molecules, they are beyond the scope of colloid chemistry. What we do mean by impurities is colloidally suspended particles of sand, mud, and miscellaneous organic matter, including bacteria, which render water unfit for drinking and household purposes.

Sand filtration takes care of much of the suspended solids in raw water, as described in Chapter 1; but since particles of colloidal size do not settle, some artificial means of making them do so had to be found. As the water enters the coagulating basin of large-scale purifying installations, a small proportion of a precipitating agent is added to it—in the neighborhood of 60 pounds to every million gallons. This agent, called a *coagulant*, is usually aluminum sulphate, which breaks up into trivalent aluminum ions (Al^{+++}) and divalent sulphate ions (SO_4^{--}). As these have strong electrical charges, they are highly efficient in neutralizing the oppositely charged colloidal particles.

The aluminum sulphate is often called "filter alum." By reacting with alkaline substances in the water it forms a "floc" or clump of aluminum hydroxide. This floc slowly sinks and carries a large part of the suspended solids with it. The effect may be considered as taking place in two steps: first, neutralization of the negatively charged particles of sand, clay, or organic matter by the Al^{+++} ions, which allows the impurities to sink either individually or after uniting into larger aggregates; second, the so-called "floc" formation, which acts as a sort of microscopic octopus, entangling the impurities and pulling them to the bottom, where they pass to sand filters. Another coagulant sometimes used is ferric sulphate. Aluminum sulphate is effective only when the water treated is neither very acid nor very alkaline. It is sometimes necessary to add appropriate chemicals to bring this condition about. Considerable time is required for thorough coagulation and settling, and in some cases the water must be kept in gradual motion. The purification is carried out in large settling basins especially constructed for this purpose (Plate IX).

Other agents, such as activated carbon, clay, and chlorine are often used in combination with filter alum to aid in removing color, odor, and taste, all of which are serious and frequently occurring water contaminants. Another important aspect of the purification process is its effectiveness in reducing the number of bacteria in the water. About half of them are disposed of by coagulation and subsequent settling; most of the others soon perish because of the lack of organic matter, on which their existence depends. Chlorine is used to destroy the bacteria that may escape the filters and to protect the purity of the water for some time afterward.

Boiler feed water containing scale-forming substances and factory wastes which carry a very high percentage of miscellaneous impurities may also be given the coagulation-filtration treatment. An especially interesting example of clarification of waste water by chemical treatment is offered by laboratory experiments on purification of the foul water obtained when ink is removed from printed paper, such as telephone books, in order to condition the pulp for re-use. The mass of paper to be reclaimed is first treated with caustic soda solution, which separates the ink from the paper fibers, and the impure water is then separated from the pulp by straining. Studies have recently been conducted to determine the practicability of removing from the water the suspended particles of fats, oils, and pigments by adding an electrolyte. About half of these particles are of colloidal size and will not, of course, settle out by gravity. It has been found that a small amount of sulphuric acid is about 99 per cent effective in coagulating the impurities by means of hydrogen ions.

Naturally the purpose of clarifying water which has

been polluted by chemical extraction processes, of which de-inking is merely one illustration, is to minimize the evil of discharging such waste products into streams and rivers where they may contaminate the water supply of other communities, and are in any case a health hazard. The offensive and sometimes dangerous sludges resulting from the operation of tanneries, petroleum refineries, paper mills, and the like are sometimes treated, but this practice is by no means general. Further work along these lines in experimental laboratories will undoubtedly result in widespread adoption of industrial waste water purification methods in the future; indeed, Federal regulations requiring it may soon be established.

Laboratory experiments differ in important respects from large-scale operations. In the laboratory it is not only quite possible, but essential, to prepare materials in such an exact way that there will be a minimum of interference from unknown factors. Experimental solutions of colloidal clays, metals, or what not can be so made up that they are known to contain only particles of the desired size; and their properties, such as temperature, acidity and viscosity, can be exactly controlled. Thus it is possible to say that such solutions will do so-and-so when exposed to such-and-such conditions, to learn specific facts and formulate laws about them. But in considering such industrial projects as municipal water purification, it is obvious that laboratory conditions cannot exist. Instead of a uniform colloidal system in which all the particles are about the same size, we have many particles of much larger dimensions as well. It is often a temptation to refer to any system containing finely divided solids as "colloidal," whereas it actually may contain a much larger proportion of microscopically visible bodies than of colloidal ones. In fact, as will be mentioned presently, some systems are so complex that they may be regarded as double colloids: not only does their particle size range run the entire gamut from true solution up to fairly large particles in suspension, but the colloids exist in different forms. In large-scale handling of water, waste fluids, and sewage it is necessary to take all sizes of contaminating bodies into consideration; the larger ones can be settled out and the small ones coagulated or precipitated by electrolytes. The point is that rarely indeed does one have uniform size distribution in any natural substance, and it is therefore erroneous to think of colloidal systems and dispersions of particles in the microscopic range as being mutually exclusive.

Nowhere is this fact more apparent than in the case of sewage disposal—a feature of community life which few of the population ever think about, yet one eminently necessary for public health and civic well being. In small towns which are near a river, the problem can be readily met by discharging the sewage directly into it. If this seems likely to interfere with the happiness of towns farther downstream, simple sand filtration, followed by chlorine treatment, is required. But by far the greater quantity of sewage in large cities must be carefully treated to remove offensive organic and mineral material from the water. Installations for this purpose require considerable space and quite an outlay of public funds.

Sewage consists of a dilute suspension of solid and semi-solid materials in water. Essentially the disposal problem resolves itself into three parts: (1) increasing the concentration of the mixture by sedimentation to produce what is known as a sludge; (2) removal of the remaining water by filtration; and (3) final disposition of the dried sludge cake. The first step in handling raw sewage is to run it into circular tanks or basins, at which point coagulating chemicals are added, as already described in connection with water purification. Ferric chloride ($FeCl_3$), a compound of iron, is the electrolyte most commonly used. As sewage is rather strongly acidic, aluminum sulfate is ineffective; moreover, iron is heavier than aluminum and so helps to carry down the heavy sludge particles. Fed into the conditioning tank as a water solution, the ferric chloride is present in the form of Fe^{+++} and Cl^- ions. Hydrated lime is sometimes used in conjunction with it, if the sewage is extremely acidic. The same neutralizing action takes place as with the colloidally suspended solids in water—for sewage conditioning is really water purification in the grand manner. The negatively charged solid particles attract the strongly positive ferric ions. This removes their "life-belts" and causes them to settle to the bottom by gravity. After the conditioning chemicals are added, the mass of liquid sewage is agitated by revolving paddle arms to insure thorough mixing.

At this point in the process a new factor enters the picture—namely, "digestion" of the sludge by bacteria and other micro-organisms. The extent to which this occurs determines the difference between "raw" sludge and "activated" sludge, and the two are handled differently. In the former case, in which Imhoff sedimentation tanks are used, the chemically conditioned sewage is allowed to sediment; the larger bodies do so by gravity and the colloidal ones by precipitation, as described above. The sediment is transferred to other tanks and the excess water from which it came is discharged to a river, either with or without filtration. The concentrated sludge remains in the second set of tanks until most of the organic matter has been partially consumed, or "digested" by bacteria; the qualifying word "partially" is used advisedly, as no oxygen is admitted to the tanks and the growth of microorganisms is thus retarded. The purpose of digestion, which is a polite expression for rotting, is to make the sludge easier to filter. After this process has gone on for awhile, the sludge is delivered to filters which separate it completely from the remaining water. It is finally disposed of in one of several ways, which include use as fertilizer, consignment to Davy Jones, and incineration. The filters are usually the simple sand-bed type already mentioned, though vacuum-drum rotary filters have been installed in several localities (see Plate X).

The "activated" sludge method makes much greater use of the digestion principle. As chemically treated sewage passes through tanks, air is blown into it, the idea being to stimulate the growth of bacteria in the sludge. It is then run into large open basins about fifteen feet deep, which are so arranged that fresh air is constantly supplied to the material.

As a result of this, the bacteria attached to the

particles of organic matter in the sludge are enabled
to thrive. The object in making life easy for them is
this: many of the suspended solid particles in the microscopic size range are prevented from settling rapidly by a film or protective layer of some such colloidal substance as albumen or other protein, and the
microorganisms feed on this material and gradually
consume a large part of it. Thus the quantity of sustaining colloidal material is reduced to the point where
the solid particles respond to gravity and sink.

Here is a case which well illustrates the complexity
of colloid chemistry. In the activated sludge process,
it is involved in two different ways: first, electrically
charged particles of colloidal size which are present in
the sewage are precipitated by the action of oppositely
charged ions; second, organic substances which are colloidal in nature and which adhere as protective coatings on larger particles are consumed by bacteria,
permitting the particles to settle out by gravity. In
sewage-sludge treatment we are dealing with a mixed
system in which solids in both the colloidal and microscopic size ranges are dispersed. It so happens that
the nature of the material causes the formation of
gelatinous coatings on the larger particles and enables
them to remain suspended in the water. On this size
level the colloidal envelope encasing the particle per-
forms the same "life-belt" duty as does the electrical
charge on the free colloidal particles. We shall have
more to say in succeeding chapters of this protective
function, which is characteristic of protein-containing
substances.

Only the barest outline of the water purification and

sewage disposal techniques has been given; a sizable book could be written about these applications of colloid chemistry alone. Here as elsewhere in this book we are primarily interested in the aspects of various industrial processes which bear most closely on the subject. For this reason unnecessary processing and engineering details have been omitted. Even the colloidal phases are only briefly described, in order to present a concise and simple survey of the entire range of this vital field of knowledge.

CHAPTER 7

Curds and Whey

o o
o

As a GROUP, the food industry and those industries closely related to it are most intimately concerned with colloid chemistry. As fats and proteins play a prominent part in nutrition and growth, and are essential constituents of the body, it is natural to suppose that these important colloids should be found in many kinds of foods, of both vegetable and animal origin. All nutrients originate from the soil and from the chemical substances which it contains, remarkably transformed by nature into life-sustaining and body-building materials. In this chapter let us look at milk and some of its products from the point of view of the colloid chemist rather than the dietitian. It is one of the most complex systems considered in this book, but it is also one of the most generally interesting, constituting as it does the background of the average person's daily food intake.

The composition of milk varies considerably, depending on the animal from which it comes. Confining the picture to cow's milk for the moment, we find that it is largely made up of four substances. The first of these is water, which comprises 87 per cent, and gives milk its characteristic fluidity. Next in the order of quantity (about 5 per cent) comes lactose, which is a kind of sugar; it forms a true solution in the water and is therefore, of course, of molecular size. The third component, the well known butter fat, is present to the extent of about 3.7 per cent. Microscopic particles of this fat varying greatly in size are dispersed throughout the water, uniformly at first but after a time rising to the surface, because of their lighter weight. The final bulk ingredient is a protein substance called casein, of which there is 3 per cent. This makes a total of 98.7 per cent. The balance is made up of lactalbumin and other proteins, traces of calcium, phosphorus, and potassium compounds, and vitamins A, B_1, B_2, C, and D. This amazing combination of nutrients makes milk a unique food substance, containing most of the energy and growth requirements of man.

It is interesting to observe that the percentage of water in milk is only a little higher than that of the human body. This water, together with the dissolved sugar, mineral elements, lactalbumin, and vitamins is commonly called "whey," but is technically referred to as "serum." This designation is not limited to milk, but is applied also to liquids of similar physical composition, like blood and rubber latex. The form of sugar which occurs in milk—lactose—is in standard use in medicine as an infant food and for treatment of cases in which there is need for a nutrient of high energy value which can be easily digested. Lactose is ideal for this purpose as it is readily assimilated by invalids.

The butter-fat globules in milk require considerable attention. For the most part they are well above the colloidal size range, though a few of them are as small as $\frac{1}{10}$ micron in diameter. Scientists classify most fats as liquids. Even though they are semi-solid at normal temperature, a few degrees' increase is sufficient to make them fluid. Furthermore, they tend to behave like liquids in numerous ways, as their molecular structure is not crystalline. As previously mentioned, a system made up of liquid particles suspended in another liquid is termed an *emulsion*; the particles may or may not be of colloidal dimensions. Milk therefore is an emulsion of butter fat in water. It is now generally believed that each globule of fat is covered with a thin layer or husk of a protein which has never been positively identified. This serves primarily to keep one globule of fat from sticking to another as they move about in the serum as a result of molecular bombardment. Many proteins are colloids of the "gel" type previously referred to. They often coat the dispersed globules of emulsions and play an important part in stabilizing them by preventing the particles from cohering, which of course would destroy the emulsion. This function has led scientists to classify whole groups of these gel-type substances—both those that contain proteins and those that do not—as *protective* colloids. The most familar of these are gelatin, gum arabic, gum karaya, and gum tragacanth, all of which are utilized in the food industries to increase the normal stabilizing function of milk proteins. The last three are obtained as exudations from certain species of trees found principally in India, and are therefore known as vegetable gums.

As everyone knows, the fat globules in milk will

gradually rise to the top of a container to form cream. The procedure can be carried out more quickly and easily in a separator—a revolving metal chamber similar to a washing machine. In the process of separation the heavier water is thrown to the outer portion of the container, where it escapes through perforations, and the comparatively light fat globules collect in concentrated solution near the center. This device, which capitalizes on the slight difference in specific gravity between two substances and separates them by centrifugal force, is widely used on both large- and small-scale projects in many different industries. As its mode of operation suggests, it is known as a *centrifuge*. It may be run at a number of speeds, depending on the amount of difference in the specific gravities and on the completeness of the separation desired.

This description of the nature of the fat globules in milk gives a clue to the reason why butter is made by churning. The effect of rapidly agitating the milk with either an old-fashioned wooden "dasher" or a modern mechanical churn is to rupture the protective coating of protein on the fat globules. This permits the butter fat to coalesce, first into aggregates and then into a mass of butter. The serum, or whey, is then drained off. The richer the milk, the easier it is to make butter from; most butter is therefore made from cream. Because of the scarcity of fat particles in skim milk, it is a poor source of butter.*

A recent development in dairy chemistry is "homogenized" milk, in which the distribution of fat par-

---

* An amusing sidelight on milk is in the report which recently emanated from Hollywood that a liquid substitute is prepared syn-

ticles remains uniform indefinitely. The larger a fat globule, the faster it will rise; and the smaller it is, the more it will be inclined to remain submerged. If *all* the larger globules could be reduced in size to the point at which the stabilizing effect of the envelope of protein would just equal the force of gravity, they would neither rise nor sink. This result is obtained by passing the milk through a machine called a homogenizer, or a "colloid mill." The particles are forced between metal faces which are extremely close together. The shearing action causes the large particles to break up into smaller ones of about the same size, which remain uniformly dispersed. Plate XI shows how a typical emulsion is affected by passing through a homogenizer. The reduction in particle size makes milk more easily digested and keeps it of uniform nutritive value throughout. Homogenizers are widely used in the ice-cream industry.

Fat globules are too large to be greatly affected by surface electrical charges, but the stabilizing influence of the protective coating is at least partly due to a characteristic peculiarity of the gel-type colloids, which accounts for their remaining in permanent suspension. They have a strong affinity for water and are technically known as "hydrophilic" or "water-loving" substances, in contradistinction to the "hydrophobic" colloids of the sol group previously mentioned. The

thetically for use in scenes in which lovely ladies are discovered taking milk baths. Dismayed at the cost of using real milk, producers have adopted the so-called Handley formula, a mixture of calcium carbonate, bismuth subnitrate, and probably some protective colloid. This is sold in concentrated form and dissolved in water. The resulting dispersion is as photogenic as milk and far cheaper.

adjacent water molecules are attracted to the exposed surface of the complex protein molecules because of the internal electrical forces present in both types of molecule. As a result, a definitely aligned water-protein layer is formed which has the same sustaining effect as external electrical charges do on solid particles. This phenomenon is called "hydration." Its exact mechanism is still a matter for study. The extent of this effect varies with the kind of protein. In cases where it is slight, it occurs in combination with external electrical charges. This water-protein union is somewhat more difficult to visualize than the surface charge idea. To use a crude but serviceable analogy, it is like the thin film of water which clings to the body of a swimmer and emerges with him when he climbs out of the lake. It is characteristic of substances like proteins which are made up of large, complicated molecules. We shall have occasion to discuss hydration again in a later chapter. In a word, then, the fat globules in milk are covered with a stabilizing layer of a hydrophilic protein which is itself a colloid of the gel type.

In handling milk in large-scale food processes where smoothness and uniform consistency are required, such as in the manufacture of candy, ice cream, and other delicacies, an additional quantity of protective material is used. To prevent confectionery from having a granular structure when a large percentage of sugar is involved, and to avoid the formation of water crystals in ice cream, about two per cent of gelatin is effective. This surrounds the fat globules with an extra-thick protective envelope. Because of its ability to "hold" water by hydration, as just described, it tends to keep the water from crystallizing out of the emulsion when frozen. A seaweed product known as algin has recently been found even better than gelatin in giving a smooth, creamy texture to ice cream, which means of course that algin is still more hydrophilic than gelatin. Other vegetable gums are also coming into use.

Proteins are extremely sensitive to heat—so much so, indeed, that their vital functions are destroyed by long exposure to high temperature. Fortunately the pasteurization process does not bother them. Here the milk is quickly heated to about 150°F—just high enough to kill the bacteria—and immediately run through a chilling system which restores it to about 40°F. If milk is boiled for even a minute or two, a portion of the protein content rises to the surface and coagulates into the heavy scum which most of us find so objectionable on over-cooked cocoa.

The protein content of milk is also largely responsible for its foaming propensity. Fresh milk as it comes from the cow is usually covered with foam; and the use of an egg-beater on whole milk or cream will soon produce a similar effect. This is directly caused by a quantity of air being trapped in the milk; but if it were not for the stiffness imparted by protein compounds, no foam would result. This is equally true of other emulsions of high protein content. Sometimes it is desirable to produce an unusually stiff or permanent foam; this again is accomplished by adding a little protective material like gum karaya. During the war when whipped cream was almost unheard of, packages of this preparation were sold in grocery stores to help the housewife realize all of the limited foaming possibilities of whole milk, or perhaps even skim milk. Much the same principle is applied in making stable soap films for shaving creams. Indeed, the whole field of bubbles and films is properly in the colloidal domain and is involved in a number of important commercial processes.

From what has been said about the protein content of milk it may be assumed that the proteins are present in several different forms. The first of these is the protective coating on the fat particles; the second is the lactalbumin, which is thought to exist in colloidal dispersion in the serum; the third form is the one important protein constituent of milk which has not yet been discussed—casein. It is generally supposed to be in chemical combination with the calcium and phosphorus, but for the sake of simplicity this fact may be passed over. Its particles are equipped with the now familiar "electrical life-belts," although hydration undoubtedly plays a part as well. Though less well known, casein is an extremely important factor in the complex colloidal system which we call milk. There is almost as much of it in a quart of milk as there is butter fat; it has a hand in foam formation; and it is directly involved in the manufacture of all kinds of cheeses.

Speaking of cheese suggests curds, which in turn implies souring. What makes milk turn sour? Certainly not a thunderstorm! It is something quite a bit more complicated. As a rule it may be said that the appearance in an organic colloidal system of even a small amount of acid is certain to cause coagulation sooner or later. The reason for this, as previously indicated, is that every such system is normally almost neutral. When an electrolyte containing hydrogen (found in all acids) is added, it at once ionizes, liberating a multitude of hydrogen ions in the solution. These first decrease the alkalinity to the neutral point, and then carry the solution over into acid territory. They also reduce the electrical potential on the casein particles, and bring them close to their isoelectric point.*

This is where the importance of temperature comes in. Even in pasteurized milk there are great numbers of bacteria which tend to give off acidic products—very slowly in cold milk, but rather rapidly as it gets warmer. These products react with the milk sugar (lactose) to form lactic acid, which in turn liberates hydrogen ions, thus raising the acidity and precipitating the casein in the form of a curd; the isolectric point of casein—where the supporting charge is fully neutralized—is at pH 4.6, which is fairly acid. The curdling of skim milk under controlled conditions—many of which are almost fantastically complicated—is the basis

---

* It should be explained that acidity and alkalinity are measured by a scale in somewhat the same way as temperature, except that the values change by a factor of ten instead of additively, representing what mathematicians know as a logarithmic or "pH" scale. This runs from 1.0 (highly acid) to 14.0 (highly alkaline); from 6.5 to 7.5 is the neutral range, 7.0 being the exact point at which a substance is neither acidic nor alkaline. These numbers are logarithmic representations of the number of hydrogen ions in the solution. Above the neutral point is the "alkaline side," the virtues of which are publicly extolled, whereas below this point the acid range begins. This is dangerous ground for colloids, as it means a close approach to the point at which the electrical lifebelts are destroyed. If positively charged hydrogen ions enter a system like milk, which is very slightly acidic (pH 6.6), there is imminent danger that they will increase the acidity sufficiently to coagulate the system. As previously explained, coagulation is caused by attraction of the positively charged ions to the negatively charged colloidal particles of casein.

of cheese manufacture. If fat globules are present when souring takes place, most of them are carried down with the casein; but the fewer there are, the more effective the curd formation will be.

Those who have literary inclinations may intrigue themselves by recalling references to colloidal phenomena in the work of poets and novelists. A number of these which have cropped up during the preparation of this book will be mentioned at appropriate places, as they afford an interesting sidelight on the scientific acumen of several renowned authors who unconsciously revealed themselves as potential colloid chemists centuries ago! The case in point at the moment occurs in the passage in *Hamlet* where the Ghost is describing his death, caused by "juice of cursed hebenon" being poured into his ear—"the leperous distillment whose effect holds such enmity to the blood of man that, swift as quicksilver . . . it doth posset and curd, like eager [*i.e.*, acid] droppings into milk, the thin and wholesome blood." This is a good Elizabethan description of the coagulation of a protein by added electrolyte!

It may be asked why milk doesn't form curds when taken into the stomach, where there is an enormously high concentration of hydrogen ions. Gastric juice contains hydrochloric acid, and is corrosive enough to eat its way through a piece of iron pipe. How the stomach wall is able to remain unaffected by it throughout a lifetime is just another instance of the natural miracles of the human body which have never been clearly understood by science. At any rate, it is probable that a form of curdling does occur in the stomach;

but the digestive system of the normal adult is somehow able to handle milk in a strongly acid medium,
curds and all.

A word may be said here about the unique nature of
human milk, which makes it particularly adapted to
the needs of the infant. Some babies cannot digest
cow's milk because of the comparatively large size of
the fat particles and the high protein content, which
forms curds in the stomach, whereupon the mixture is
usually "precipitated" onto the bed! Human milk contains a much higher percentage of sugar than cow's
milk (though the latter can easily be supplemented
with lactose). The protein content of human milk is
only one-third that of cow's milk, which accounts for
its greater digestibility. The fat contents of the two
are about equal.

Returning to the discussion of casein, we find that
this cheesy protein has so many important uses that
producing it in pure form is quite an industry in itself.
On a commercial scale it is made from skim milk. Because of our habit in the United States of throwing
most of our whey to the pigs, we have consistently been
forced to import casein for industrial purposes from
Argentina. The skim milk is most often coagulated
with some strong acid, such as sulphuric or hydrochloric. For certain special uses, however, a catalytic
substance called rennet is more satisfactory. Rennet is
an enzyme present in the digestive system of calves,
and is closely related chemically to pepsin. It does such
an effective job of coagulation that as little as one part
of rennet can separate the casein from four million
parts of slightly acid skim milk. The principal applica-

tion for rennet casein is in the manufacture of plastic products.

The demand for casein steadily increased during the twenty years before the war. The estimated total consumption in this country rose from 19 million pounds in 1917 to 73 million pounds in 1937. Of the latter quantity 67 million pounds was domestically produced and only about 6 million imported. This is quite a contrast to 1917, when the imports were actually higher than home production. This is indeed a prodigious amount of casein! Where does it all go?

In the neighborhood of 3.5 million pounds of it are used in the manufacture of casein-base paints. These are the popular water paints which have come into general use in the last few years for kitchens, bathrooms, and other jobs where a dull or "flat" finish and pastel colors are satisfactory. In the chemical sense, you might almost as well use a water solution of welsh rarebit! Casein paint has certain advantages for interior work, not the least of which are that it can readily be applied with a roller or brush by the diligent housewife, that it can easily be wiped up when spattered, and can be kept clean by judicious washing. It is also free from the objectionable odor of turpentine and naphtha which is characteristic of oil paints. Its poor resistance to weathering makes it inadvisable for use on exterior surfaces, unless only temporary results are needed. Huge quantities were used to coat many of the buildings at the World's Fair in 1939.

An even larger use of casein on a tonnage basis is in the coating of fine paper. When mixed with clay or other mineral filler and water, casein is admirably suited to fill in the chinks between the pulp fibers and to provide a firm, glossy base on which the finest halftones can be clearly reproduced. An outstanding advantage of the casein finish over starch and glue, which are also used, is that it makes the paper waterproof to the point where it can be washed with a wet sponge. Much the same finishing properties make casein suitable for treating leather goods and similar articles.

Glues made from casein—or any other protein, for that matter—demonstrate a property of the gel-type colloids which will be touched on later in more detail: stickiness. Many proteins make excellent commercial adhesives, and of these casein is one of the most widely used. It has been in increasing demand for this purpose since 1917, when casein glues were introduced. It is strong, water-resistant, and easy to apply; but it is subject to deterioration by molds and high humidity. It works especially well in wood assemblies and has been successfully used in aircraft and automobile bodies—as well as in plywood for general construction in the woodworking industries, particularly where the structure is curved, as in pianos, motor boats, and roof supports. When correctly used it is stronger than most animal glues. Shortly after World War I extensive experiments in the aircraft field were carried out on wood bonded with casein compositions. These were considered promising at the time for small private planes; but in more recent years casein has been largely supplanted for this purpose by synthetic-resin adhesives. Much of the development work on casein glues for wood products was done at the Forest Products Laboratory in Madison, Wisconsin, which is the national headquarters for wood technology. Casein is also used as a binder for ground cork, wood flour, and similar dry materials which must be united and pressed into sheet form.

Of recent years we have grown accustomed to sensational news stories about scientific developments and glowing descriptions of the unparalleled marvels of the world of tomorrow. One of the miracles which has been proclaimed at regular intervals during the last decade to mystify the lay public is "buttons, buckles, and clothing made from milk." It is true, of course, that milk is the starting point for these products, but this statement is as much of an exaggeration as it would be to say that beefsteak and potatoes are made out of dirt, or ashes out of air. The same applies to other generalities about synthetic products, which are put forward rather to amaze and baffle than to inform.

Casein which has been prepared with the enzyme rennet is used in large quantities in the manufacture of miscellaneous plastic articles. The casein is usually ground to a fine powder; water is then added, together with the colors and other modifying agents desired; and the whole is kneaded mechanically into a viscous mass. It is then run through an "extrusion" machine, which operates on the meat-grinder principle, and the material comes out in the form of a smooth rod or bar (it may also be extruded in any shape possible to attain with the dies adapted to the process). At this point it is still in the raw or "green" state. To fit it for practical use, the rods or shapes are passed through a bath of formaldehyde. The hardening effect of this chemical on proteins is exactly what makes it useful as embalming fluid. After this treatment the casein mix feels like a piece of petrified wood or ivory and can be sliced up and machined in any desired way.

As early as 1890 Adolph Spitteler, a German chemist, made what was undoubtedly the first casein plastic —a "white blackboard" for classroom use—by coagulating milk and mixing the casein curd with formaldehyde. The chief use of casein plastics today is in garment buttons, decorative buckles, cigarette holders, and the like. One reason for the popularity of casein was that it could be made in bright, attractive colors at a time when other plastic materials could not. With the advent of color in formaldehyde-base plastics the use of casein for most plastic applications may be expected to diminish.

Some years ago an Italian scientist, Antonio Ferretti, found that casein mixtures could be extruded in the form of continuous filaments in the same way as rayon and nylon. When run through a formaldehyde bath the casein threads become so strong that they can be woven into fabrics which are water-repellent and about as warm as wool, which they greatly resemble chemically. A good deal was made of this discovery in a publicity sense; and it is a fact that serviceable fabrics and wearing apparel have been made of casein in considerable volume. The material was known as "Lanital" (Italian wool), and production was carried on in Italy up to 1941. Patents have also been secured in the United States, and a comparable American product is now sold under the trade name "Aralac." This is usually combined about half and half with natural wool, cotton, or rayon.

Besides its application in the fields so far noted, casein has a number of miscellaneous uses. In food preparations and other types of emulsions it is a good protective colloid, and it even has some medicinal value. To some extent it has been applied to the sizing of textile fibers, and it is an ingredient of certain kinds of cosmetic creams and ointments. All in all, it is a most versatile and industrially valuable substance, to which this résumé cannot possibly do justice. But for adequate knowledge of colloid chemistry, it is probable that few of these many beneficial uses would ever have been possible.

CHAPTER 8

The Tears of the Weeping Tree

○   ○

○

Tᴴɪꜱ ꜱᴏᴍᴇᴡʜᴀᴛ ᴍᴇʟᴀɴᴄʜᴏʟʏ title may be justified by pointing out that the native word for rubber is "caoutchouc" (pronounced "cow-chuck"), which means "tree that weeps." The sorrows of this particular botanical species have provided mankind with another wondrous and highly complex natural substance in the form of a unique kind of sap called latex. It is obtained by tapping, which involves cutting into the tree to a layer just below the bark, from which the latex slowly oozes, to be collected in cups attached to the tree. In appearance, latex is much like milk, and it also is an emulsion comprised of protein-coated particles of rubber dispersed in a serum which is almost wholly water. The normal content of rubber particles is about 35 per cent of the latex; of the balance, 60 per cent is water, 2 per cent is protein, and 2 per cent sugars.

The particles of protein-covered rubber are much smaller than most of the fat globules in milk, and are in the upper range of colloidal dimensions. As might be expected, they are in constant Brownian movement and are stabilized chiefly by negative electrical charges, although the water layer on the surface may play a secondary part. So sensitive is the latex system that it will coagulate after standing for only twelve hours, be-

118

cause of the putrefying action of acid-forming bacteria. For this reason ammonia is usually added to latex on the plantations to preserve it during shipment and storage (ammonia is a strong "base," which raises the pH from about 7.5 to 10). This allows an adequate margin of safety for the slow release of hydrogen ions resulting from acidic products of bacteria, and from chance contamination with impurities in the iron drums in which the latex is shipped. Many a disappointment has been caused by improperly washed or corroded containers. Imagine opening a valuable cargo of latex only to find it a clotted mass of rubber gum and water!

Latex is coagulated in tanks on the plantations if dry rubber is wanted, or it may be concentrated before shipment to manufacturers for use in liquid form. Coagulation is usually brought about by adding a little acetic or formic acid; less often salt is used. The ionization and electrical discharge mechanism is the same as previously described. The serum is then discarded and the rubber washed, sheeted, and smoked or crêped.

Now let us take a closer look at the particles themselves. They are only visible in the ultramicroscope by virtue of the "twinkling effect" caused by reflected light; in the electron microscope, however, they appear as large as marbles. Careful studies of their structure have shown that they are usually round or slightly pear-shaped, and that they are made up of a central core of liquid rubber, an intermediate layer of solid rubber, and a rather thick layer of a protein which is probably albumin. This is one of the hydrophilic substances like casein, which are intimately bound up with the surrounding water molecules. It undoubtedly aids

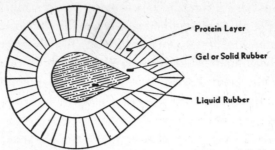

From Davis and Blake, *Chemistry and Technology of Rubber*

FIG. 20 *Supposed structure of a particle of natural rubber latex.*

in stabilizing the latex, and helps to prevent the particles from sticking together as a result of chance collisions due to their rapid motion. In the main, however, the negative charges on the particles are the important factor, as with casein in milk.

Cream readily forms on milk because of the large size of the fat globules. Because latex particles are so much smaller, they rise to the surface extremely slowly; a rubber "cream" on latex requires weeks to form. As it is commercially desirable to have latex in as concentrated a solution as possible, both to save shipping space and to produce articles of high quality, some rapid means of inducing the latex to cream became necessary (see Plate XIII). Three methods of doing this have been used on a large scale. One of these is the centrifuge, which must be operated at a speed of about 8000 r.p.m. for effective results, because the specific gravity of the particles is very little less than that of water. Even under the best conditions only the larger particles are separated, most of the smaller ones being left behind. Notwithstanding its drawbacks, centrifuging has been rather widely used. It gives a latex of about 60 per cent rubber content, roughly double the concentration of the natural form. Latex concentrates as high as 75 per cent of rubber content are obtained by merely evaporating off the water. This product is marketed under the trade name of "Revertex." *

The most interesting method of creaming from the standpoint of colloid chemistry is that in which colloidal substances of the gel, or "water-loving," type are added to the latex soon after it comes from the tree. Gelatin, casein, and vegetable gums do the trick, and even glue can be used. What happens is this. The rate at which the particles of rubber rise is proportional to their size; therefore if the latex particles could be made larger they would cream very readily. By adding a protein complex which is soluble in water this increase in diameter is easily brought about. The added material sticks to the protein coating of the particle in sufficient quantity to enlarge it tremendously. In this way it not only sustains the particle but hoists it to the surface, like pontoons under a water-logged submarine. The process may be repeated half a dozen times to meet specific requirements.

For most practical uses latex must be vulcanized or "cured." This means that sulphur and other dry chemicals must be mixed into it in small proportions. For many industrial purposes rather large amounts of powders and pigments must also be incorporated. Among these are carbon black, clay, and whiting. Here we have a delicate problem in applied colloid chem-

* Product of the Revertex Corporation of America, Brooklyn, N. Y.

istry, for unconcentrated latex is so "touchy" that addition of dry powders is likely to cause coagulation. To secure proper blending it is necessary to do two things. First, wet the particles of powder with a water solution of a water-absorbing colloid such as gelatin, casein, or albumin, so that each solid particle will be coated with a protective film of protein. Then pass the solid-liquid mixture through a homogenizer, or colloid mill, in which the shearing action of the closely rotating parts breaks up the solid pigment particles into a standard, uniform size (the protective material will surround each of these after the milling operation). The homogenized mix is then added to a latex concentrated to about 50 per cent rubber content. The compounding of latex is a ticklish process which demands a high degree of skill, knowledge, and precise control, as well as strict uniformity of materials. The action of the colloid mill in dispersing vulcanizing agents, solid fillers, and pigments—collectively known as "compounds" —is shown in Plate XII.

The most common method of making rubber articles from latex after it has been compounded in the above manner is by dipping suitably shaped forms into a bath of concentrated latex and then withdrawing them and allowing them to dry. The cycle is repeated as many times as necessary to secure the desired thickness. This differs from the electrodeposition process described earlier in that no electric current is passed through the latex. However, there are many factors affecting the quality of the final product. Chief among these are the concentration of the latex and the rate at which the forms are introduced and withdrawn. Sixty per cent latex is usually the best, and fairly slow removal of the forms is essential. A great deal of work has been done to determine the ideal conditions for efficient dipping; for of course the faster the process is performed the more economical it is, provided that the finished products are satisfactory. One means of accelerating it in making toy balloons is to coat the metal forms with an acid. This of course immediately coagulates the latex as it touches the form, and makes it possible to manufacture the article with only one immersion. It is an interesting fact that the natives of Brazil made clothing and balls by hand-dipping hundreds of years ago, and that modern science has been able to speed up the process no less than 150 times. Even a method which looks as simple to the uninitiated as sticking a form into rubber latex, pulling it out, and letting the water evaporate requires untold weeks of experimentation and study by experts before effective commercial techniques can be developed. Colloidal systems are seldom easy to handle; they demand infinite patience and years of training to manipulate successfully.

The manufacture of porous articles from latex has recently undergone considerable development. Kneeling pads, automobile seat cushions, and even mattresses of invitingly soft texture and "give" have been on the market for some years, the latter under the trade name "Airfoam." * These are made directly from concentrated and compounded latex which has been agitated in an oversize mixing bowl until a stable froth has formed. As with milk, the proteins in the latex make it highly susceptible to foaming when air is beaten into it.

* Product of Goodyear Tire and Rubber Company, Akron, Ohio.

Usually some soap solution is added to keep the foam stiff until coagulation has occurred. Latex froth so prepared is a delightful-looking product, which pours softly from the container into the curing molds like so much smooth whipped cream. Coagulation sets in either before or during vulcanization, depending on the method used.

In the last twenty years the use of concentrated latex by the rubber industry has greatly increased, as for many special kinds of articles it is a much better raw material than solid crude rubber. To make the latter into a liquid for manufacturing purposes, such as coating fabrics, impregnating textiles, and making extremely thin products, it is necessary to dissolve it in naphtha or a similar organic solvent. This involves time and expense, and the solution is not nearly as easy to process as latex. The discovery that latex could be kept from coagulating during shipment by preserving it with ammonia was largely responsible for the rapid increase in its use in American rubber factories. Obviously it is the most economical way of making such mechanical goods as toy ballons, surgeon's gloves, rubber panties for infants, and a host of similar articles.

As a single example of the advantage of latex over solid rubber, take the case of rubber thread, for which there is increasing demand. Formerly it had to be cut from a strip of vulcanized sheet in short lengths; the result was ragged edges, high cost, and generally poor efficiency, as high-grade sheet is extremely hard to cut exactly, even when frozen. In making it directly from latex, however, the process works like a charm: the latex is run through a small opening in a nozzle-like contrivance, which is usually made of glass, but occasionally of gold. Emerging in the form of a thread, it passes through a tank of coagulant fluid, and is then dried and wound on spools, all in one operation. A spool weighing only a pound may carry as much as *ten miles* of rubber thread in a single length. Prevulcanized latex, known to the trade as "Vultex," * may be used for this purpose.

Coating tire fabric cords and sometimes the fabric itself is an established application of latex. Interesting possibilities in tire manufacture are presented by the use of cloth made of woven glass fibers—which looks and feels so much like cotton duck that it is almost indistinguishable. Latex has also been tried in wood pulp for the production of waterproof paper, and in various other specialties, such as covering wire mesh and metal parts with rubber by the electrodeposition process, previously described.

In all the applications so far mentioned the latex must eventually be vulcanized, or cured; otherwise it would deteriorate rapidly and would have no strength. But there is one use of rubber, in both solid and liquid forms, which does not require vulcanization, as it depends on the natural stickiness of the rubber itself— the stickiness that at least partially accounts for the effectiveness of friction tape and surgeon's plaster. Latex is one of the best adhesives for special purposes that has ever been discovered. This seems to be due partly to its protein content and partly to the structure of the basic molecule isoprene. At any rate, either

* Product of the General Latex and Chemical Corporation, Cambridge, Massachusetts.

ordinary latex or the cured "Vultex" makes a spec-
tacularly good adhesive bond for rubber surfaces. It is
the best means of repairing rubber belting, which is
made up of layers of rubber-coated cotton duck. If a
break occurs, or if two lengths of belt are to be united,
the layers are cut back stepwise in corresponding positions on opposite sides of the belt, and a liberal coat of
vulcanized latex applied. After drying, the ends are
fitted together and firmly clamped until the adhesive
has "set." To test the strength of the bond, the strip of
belt is placed in a breaking machine, the jaws of which
are gradually separated more and more. A six-ply belt
spliced with "Vultex" will break at a tension of over a
hundred thousand pounds at a point *outside* the splice.
And that takes a pretty good adhesive!

Unvulcanized latex has long been used in the leather
industry as an adhesive in shoe soles, its affinity for
leather being even greater than for rubber. Here it is
applied in its natural concentration of about 30 per
cent rubber content. In conjunction with blood albumin, latex has been used as a bonding agent between
vulcanized rubber and metal surfaces where a large
iron connection or "nipple" must be built into the end
of a length of oil-loading or fire-engine hose. Blood,
incidentally, is not a bad adhesive in its own right.
Latex is also blended with casein to form a tenacious
glue sold under the trade name of "Casco." * Marked
improvement in the mechanical properties of tar and
asphalt for road surfacing purposes has been achieved
by blending them with latex by a rather complicated
technique which it is unnecessary to describe. This is an

* Product of the Casein Company of America, New York, N. Y.

ingenious application of rubber indeed, for ordinary rubber paving slabs have been costly failures in the few experiments that have been tried. By mixing latex directly with the asphalt a kind of duplex surface is obtained in which each material helps to overcome the defects of the other, while retaining its own advantages.

No discussion of rubber latex could make any pretense to completeness without some mention of synthetic latices. As this at once involves the phenomenon of polymerization, which is also the basis of almost the entire plastics industry, we may consider for a moment the outstanding facts about it. Synthetic organic plastic products in general are made by reacting common and cheap materials such as carbon, chlorine, benzene, formaldehyde, acetylene, and oxygen with a catalyst under conditions of high heat and pressure. The purpose of the catalyst, as explained in Chapter 1, is to accelerate the rate of the reaction tremendously, though the catalyst itself remains unaffected. The most generally effective catalysts in the synthesis of rubber-like substances, high-grade aviation fuels, and plastics are finely powdered metals and their compounds—sodium, aluminum chloride, nickel, silver, and vanadium pentoxide. Their action is a special phase of colloid chemistry depending largely on surface irregularities.

Polymerization is a technical term denoting the union of a great number of small molecules to form a few much larger ones. At some stage it must occur in nature, for rubber, cellulose, starch, and proteins are natural polymers, or groups of simpler molecules chemically united. The element oxygen frequently acts as the link which holds the simple molecules together in the chain. As a result, we have macromolecules which, because of their size, belong in the domain of colloid chemistry. The research done in the United States on polymerization—the factors affecting it, the best raw materials to use, the ideal catalysts, the most effective time, temperature, and pressure of reaction, and dozens of other details—almost staggers the imagination. Polymerization is above all else the source of man's success in duplicating or improving on nature's products, and its evidences are scattered far and wide in every corner of the country, if not in the world.

Now to be more specific about synthetic rubber. The type in most general use at present is the so-called Buna, originally developed in Germany. It is made either from alcohol or from various hydrocarbons such as butane which are converted by catalytic methods to butadiene. But this is only half the picture. Another synthetic material must be reacted with butadiene to yield a satisfactory rubber. This is derived from benzene and ethylene, which react with aluminum chloride as catalyst to form a product that can be readily converted to styrene. When butadiene and styrene are blended in varying proportions, they are made into a water emulsion stabilized with soap, and are then polymerized to the final product—a synthetic rubber latex, which is coagulated with acid in the usual way. In the German method of making Buna, water emulsions were not used, but mixtures of butadiene and styrene were polymerized into synthetic rubber in the absence of water using sodium metal as a catalyst. This is where the synthetic product got its name—"bu" for butane plus "Na," the chemical symbol for sodium. This is only one of many types of synthetic rubber. Another, developed in the United States by the Du Pont Company in 1931, is derived from acetylene and chlorine; chemists call it polychloroprene, but it is better known as *neoprene*. This is also prepared in the form of latex (see Plate XIV).

Synthetic latices differ from the natural in one outstanding respect—their particles are very much smaller and of more uniform size. Indeed, they start out in about the same condition as natural latex particles achieve after being processed in a colloid mill. As a result, synthetic latex is more stable, is less likely to coagulate unexpectedly, and gives better coatings on textiles and similar materials. A general rule in the process industries is that, other things being equal, a more uniform material is a better material. Synthetic latex can be used for all the purposes mentioned above for the natural product. One of its chief applications is for coating tire fabrics.

CHAPTER 9

Blood

ο ο
ο

Wʜᴇɴ ᴅᴇsᴄʀɪʙɪɴɢ the colloidal systems that occur in nature it is hard to refrain from using such adjectives as "marvelous," "amazing," and "incomparable," so dear to the hearts of advertising copy writers. Yet complicated liquids like milk and latex do indeed confound the imagination, not only in their final state but in their creation from the crude raw materials at the disposal of nature—water, carbon dioxide, oxygen, and half a dozen key mineral elements. To these unique systems must be added the life-sustaining blood, which in its way is quite as miraculous.

Blood may be regarded as a circulating *tissue* containing 78 per cent of water. Living tissue is, of course, made up of cells. As everyone knows, the dilute tissue known as blood contains two quite different kinds of cell, one of which is dyed red, the other being without color. These two types of cell have radically different functions: the red corpuscles, which greatly outnumber their pale brethren the "white" cells, serve as a positive agent in transporting food products, oxygen, and carbon dioxide through the body; the white corpuscles, though usually inert, act as guardians against invading bacteria, which they absorb and thus remove from the system. This useful function has won them the name of "phagocytes," or "germ-eaters." A third kind of cell structure is the blood platelet, which contains essential proteins and other factors, but whose exact function is unknown.

Now all these cellular bodies are vastly larger than colloidal particles, and definitely belong in the microscopic size group. They correspond very roughly in dimensions to the larger fat globules in milk. But other particles exist in blood in sizes which are in many cases colloidal. We now are familiar enough with these complex natural systems to expect the presence of a number of proteins, in addition to a swarm of sugars and dissolved mineral compounds. Sure enough, all these substances are there. The most important from the colloidal standpoint are four proteins: albumin, which also occurs in many other mixtures; gamma-globulin, which has been found to contain valuable disease-preventing principles, or "antibodies;" and fibrinogen and prothrombin, which provide the astonishingly ingenious mechanism of coagulation. Besides these, there are other as yet unidentified proteins which are now the subject of intensive medical research. In addition to all this, salts of sodium, potassium, and other metals, as well as some glucose, are present in true solution.

Blood can be separated into its several components by the centrifuge—that is, the corpuscular bodies may be removed by the same method used in concentrating the fat in milk. However, it was not until World War II that it became essential to remove the red and white corpuscles on anything approaching a large-scale basis. Separation for biological and research purposes usually demands the use of an ultracentrifuge, which is capable of 50,000 revolutions a minute and develops a centrifugal force several thousand times that of gravity. It is not necessary to use such terrific speeds as this merely to remove the cell bodies, as these are large enough to be concentrated by cream-separator methods. The ultracentrifuge is limited to machines of laboratory size like the one shown in Plate XV. Such portions of the blood as the gamma-globulin and other protein fractions just mentioned can be separated for medical purposes only by this drastic centrifugal treatment.

A centrifuging action takes place within the body of an aviator when he is "pulling out" of a power dive. As the plane descends almost vertically, and then abruptly changes direction at better than a 90° angle at terrific speed, the tendency of the blood—and indeed of the whole body—is to maintain the original downward direction. As a result, the blood is still going toward the earth for several seconds after the plane has made its turn and started upward. This causes it to drain out of the pilot's head with great rapidity, and often results in the familiar "blackout" to which dive bombers are subject. A force of from ten to twelve times that of gravity must be withstood by the aviator under such conditions. In air service parlance this force is referred to as so many "G's."

When the platelets and the red and white corpuscles have been eliminated from whole blood, the balance of the material is the *plasma*, which performed such miracles of life-saving in the recent war. Plasma contains proteins in colloidal suspension, together with the salts, glucose, and mineral compounds. There are several reasons why plasma, rather than whole blood, is used for emergency shock treatment. First, there is the matter of spoilage; whole blood, like milk, must be kept at about 40° F to prevent decomposition, and this of course is virtually impossible under war conditions. Again, it is well known that not all people can accept any "type" of blood corpuscle, and the difficulty of establishing types and correctly matching them would be insurmountable. The absence of corpuscles from plasma does away with typing altogether. Moreover, many kinds of wounds, especially those caused by burns, result in leakage of plasma through the tissues; the large corpuscles are dialyzed out by the damaged membranes and remain in the body while the plasma escapes. This process is sometimes called "transudation." The patient's critical need is for new plasma to provide a circulating medium for the dried-out corpuscles which remain stranded in his veins. Plasma can be shipped or stored in powdered form and made ready for use at a moment's notice by adding water. In hospitals, where laboratory conditions can be maintained, whole blood may be stored in a "blood bank," to be administered with proper precautions in transfusions.

Plasma can be further centrifuged to remove the coagulating protein fibrinogen. As its name suggests, this is a thread-like structure, and its presence in plasma is essential for healing and recuperative purposes. When the fibrinogen is absent, the remaining fluid constitutes blood *serum*.

All forms of blood—whole, plasma, and serum—are practically neutral; the pH is close to 7.3, and any variation of more than a slight amount is certain to cause death. There are several rather well known diseases of the blood: an excess of sugar causes diabetes; a deficiency of red corpuscles brings on anemia; and an excess of white corpuscles induces an incurable condition known as leukemia. As has been recently publicized, both red and white cells are attacked by the neutrons released in atomic disintegration, and workers must be shielded by barriers of water or lead, which free neutrons have difficulty in penetrating. Rapid deterioration of the red corpuscles is caused by the venom of rattlesnakes and other vipers.

Just what are the red corpuscles? They are made up of a protein-mineral combination, and are thought to be "manufactured" in bone marrow. The portion of the red cell most interesting to the colloid chemist is hemoglobin—a sort of duplex substance, part mineral and part protein, which has several important functions. It is the coloring matter of blood. The mineral part of its molecule is built around the element iron, in a manner strikingly similar to the structure of the molecule of chlorophyll, the green dye found in all vegetation— except that here the central metallic element is magnesium. The striking parallel existing between hemoglobin and chlorophyll has been the subject of considerable research on plant life and growth. Iron is therefore essential for healthy blood—so there may be some good in spinach, after all.

But hemoglobin has a more important duty than merely to act as a dye: it has the ability to pick up molecules of certain gases and circulate them in the system. It is this property that makes it a unique substance in the wondrous biological mechanism that comprises the human body. As the blood is pumped outward from the heart and circulates through the spongy tissues of the lungs, the hemoglobin molecules hook onto the oxygen molecules taken in by breathing in much the same way as a bucket conveyor picks up sand or earth. In this form it is called *oxyhemoglobin*, and its color is the bright red characteristic of arterial blood. As this triple molecule travels on through the body, the oxygen is gradually burned away in the combustion of food products and is replaced by carbon dioxide. This is at once picked up and transported by the hemoglobin on its return trip through the veins. In this stage blood has a dull, bluish tinge. The carbon dioxide is dropped off at the lungs, where it is exhaled, and the cycle is repeated.

Unfortunately, such gases as carbon monoxide and methane have an even stronger affinity for hemoglobin than has oxygen. This accounts for their deadly effect. As long as a person is inhaling exhaust or illuminating gases, the hemoglobin will pick them up in preference to oxygen, and death by asphyxiation will soon result. Recovery is usually quick, once access to oxygen is provided. The insidious nature of poisoning by these gases is due to the complete absence of pain or any other warning signal; many a man has dropped dead on the floor of his garage after leaving his engine running while a stiff breeze prevented the escape of the exhaust gases from the open door. Untold deaths would have been prevented if nature had made it harder for hemoglobin to attach itself to carbon monoxide; but then, nature was unaware of the perils of modern civilization!

We have had occasion to use the word "coagulate"

very frequently in a way which is generally unfamiliar —namely, to describe the aggregation or precipitation of the particles of any colloidal suspension resulting from cancellation of electrical charges. As applied to blood, however, it refers to a quite different mechanism for accomplishing the same purpose—an interesting case, in the semantic sense, of a word whose specialized meaning is better known than its general one. The coagulation or clotting of blood is a clever device thoughtfully provided by nature to prevent one from bleeding to death from the slightest injury. Failure of the blood to clot is by no means a rare condition; it is especially prevalent among royal families where intermarriage has been practiced for centuries, and the unhappy scion must live in constant dread of pin-pricks and minor scratches. This abnormality is known as *hemophilia* and it is reported to be responsible for 10,000 deaths yearly in the United States.

The counterpart of hemophilia is a morbid tendency of the blood to form clots within the circulatory system, which causes instant death when the clot reaches the heart. Called thrombosis in its less acute stage and embolism in its fatal form, this disease has been successfully combatted with the recently discovered substance dicoumarin, which is extracted from hay. Administration of this drug has been effective in reducing the death rate from abnormal blood-clotting almost to the vanishing point. However, the situation must be taken in time, before the clot blocks a vital artery.

Two proteins, fibrinogen and prothrombin, are responsible for the clotting mechanism, which is as deft and intricate as it is effective. Prothrombin is an enzyme, or organic catalyst, which changes into thrombin under certain conditions to be mentioned in a moment. Having done so, it reacts with the fibrinogen to form fibrin, which entangles the red corpuscles into a turgid mass or clot. Why does this not happen in the bloodstream? It is the view of authentic students that the clue to this puzzle lies in the existence in the blood of two additional proteins, heparin and antithrombin. As long as these are present, the prothrombin is kept from assuming its active form; in this way they may be regarded as inhibitors of coagulation, standing guard over the system and restraining chemical changes in the blood. How then does the coagulation take place? According to the theory, these two inhibitors are *removed* from the blood by combining with a substance called cephalin which is given off by the damaged or ruptured tissues. The immediate result of an injury is a series of reactions, as follows:

1. cephalin is liberated from the wounded tissue;
2. heparin and antithrombin combine with it chemically and are thus removed;
3. prothrombin, an enzyme ferment, is then free to form thrombin;
4. thrombin causes fibrinogen to become fibrin;
5. red corpuscles, enmeshed by fibrin, harden to a clot, which seals the wound.

Oxygen seems to play no part in this phenomenon, although the effect is apparently similar to the drying of linseed oil paint, which is essentially an oxidation process. In fact, coagulation is not greatly different from polymerization; it basically involves combination of smaller, less complicated protein molecules into a much larger and more complicated form which is undoubtedly a macromolecule. Polymerization is a fact of nature, and was not invented by man. Scientists have only learned to imitate nature in their synthetic processes, and in some cases have gone her one better; but in this instance nature is unique.

To return for a moment to the subject of hemophilia and prolonged hemorrhage, we may well mention some interesting antidotes for this extremely serious breakdown in the coagulation cycle. There is in rattlesnake venom a principle called hemolysin. By extracting this and applying it in solution to minor wounds which refuse to stop bleeding in less than twenty minutes or so, it has been found that coagulation occurs within seventeen seconds. This is now a recognized method of treating hemophilia. Once more Shakespeare's prescience comes to mind: in the passage previously quoted he refers to the clotting of the "thin and wholesome blood" by a strong poison. The total destruction of blood cells by snake venom is quite unlike coagulation, however, as it involves a complete and rapid degeneration of the corpuscles. Vitamin K, extracted from alfalfa and fishmeal, is known to have anti-hemorrhagic properties, since it controls the formation of prothrombin in the liver. It is used therapeutically for this purpose by internal dosage. A recently isolated blood protein, which as yet is unnamed, is also claimed to be extremely effective in reducing coagulation time.

Blood research is one of the most active fields of biochemical study at present. One of the leaders in this field is Dr. Edwin J. Cohn of the Harvard Medical

School. New components are constantly being discovered and new applications worked out. The multitude of colloidal proteins and the equally important mineral salts constitute an inviting and highly valuable source of knowledge for biologists, and much may come of it.

CHAPTER 10

Glues and Adhesives

o   o

o

It has been said * that definitions are made by man and ignored by nature. Of course, they are all very well in a general way, and in the study of science they can be most helpful, if used with proper precaution; yet they are sometimes both ludicrous and inadequate. A famous instance of the ludicrous type is Dr. Johnson's satirical description of oatmeal as a cereal "which the Scotch use as a food, but which in England is fed to horses." Many an inadequate and even ridiculous definition has been solemnly propounded in textbooks and over lecture tables. On a somewhat more advanced plane, conflicts over basic definitions of apparently simple qualities and processes are continually rocking the scientific edifice, if not quite to its foundations, at least to its nether stories. The exact meaning of such terms as "hardness," "vulcanization," "catalysis"— even of "colloid" itself—is still open to argument.

This chapter is devoted to adhesives—yet few scientists would care to be quoted on a strict definition of what adhesion is. A general, but quite inadequate, one is that adhesion is the permanent or temporary sticking together of two substances; an adhesive is any material that will stick more or less strongly to another. These

* Professor Charles R. Plunkett, a well known authority on biology.

statements are all but worthless, as they merely substitute "stick together" for "adhere;" yet the property of stickiness is universally familiar.

Since glue was the substance from which colloid chemistry was named, and played an important part in Graham's early experiments, it boasts a unique distinction among the common materials of daily life, in addition to its elusiveness of definition. Up to fairly recent times the words "glue" and "adhesive" were used interchangeably. Now, however, glue is only *one* kind of substance which displays stickiness and adherent strength. Its history is long and interesting. Though we are asked to believe that everything was known and used by man in the Stone Age, to judge from historical résumés which invariably accompany treatises on dyes, inks, paints, textiles, metals, and numerous other substances, it is an established fact that glues of excellent quality were found still in good condition in the tomb of Tut-Ankh-Amen, where they were immured at least 3500 years ago. These glues were undoubtedly made from the hides or bones of animals, as is still done today. They were used to bond the joints of articles of furniture, caskets, and other imperial equipment of Egyptian rulers. Their preservation over so long a time is probably due to the lack of oxygen within the tombs, and to the very slight changes in temperature and humidity.

Glue was used as a coating for writing paper when it was first made in China around 100 A.D. Centuries ago it was used in Europe by expert craftsmen in the manufacture of violins and other musical instruments, a few of which are still in use. In 1690 glue was first made on a commercial scale in Holland, and the industry had its beginnings in the United States in 1808, when Elijah Upton established the American Glue Company of Boston. Before the start of the present century, however, animal and fish glues were the only types known, and little advance in the technique of manufacture or application had been made since the days of the Egyptians. Furniture making, bookbinding, specialty woodworking, and various kinds of sizing were almost the only uses for adhesives until the introduction of superior types about twenty years ago —an advance for which World War I was largely responsible.

An idea of the magnitude of the adhesives industry can be gained from the production figures of recent years. In 1924, a total of 100 million pounds of animal glue was made in the United States, plus 5 million pounds of fish glue. Five years later, there were 106 million pounds of animal glue, 5 million of fish glue, 7 million of casein glue, and no less than 133 million of various vegetable glues, chiefly from soybean and tapioca (cassava). In 1937 these figures had jumped to 122 million for animal glue, 8 million for casein glue, and 230 million for vegetable glues.

The coming of age of the airplane between 1914 and 1925 brought about a veritable revolution in the field of automotive engineering. When wooden planes were introduced on an experimental basis, adhesives at once assumed an importance of the first magnitude; and developments in this field are still actively continuing. Startling truths are now well known: that not only wood but other materials like glass fiber, metals, plastics, paper, and textiles can be "stuck together" by adhesives that produce bonds having greater strength than the materials themselves; and that thin layers of wood, with grains running at right angles, united by special adhesives and press-molded to any form, make a laminated assembly that, on a weight-for-weight basis, is one of the strongest materials known to man. Entire units for aircraft, power boats, and other structural purposes where light weight and great strength are essential can be cast in one piece, and are impervious to weather, moisture, and shock. What the first World War started came to full fruition in the second, for many of the advances in adhesive technique were put to use in defeating the Axis, and still others were made during the conflict.

As previously mentioned, the use of casein glues for aircraft and general woodworking commenced about 1917 and continued experimentally for some years. Gradually, however, adhesives prepared from synthetic resins, which had been introduced by Dr. Leo Hendrik Baekeland as early as 1912, were found to be far superior, since they are not only stronger but are free from the chief drawbacks of casein, namely, water absorption and deterioration due to bacterial action. An entire new chapter in the technology of adhesives has been written in the last few years by the sensational properties of these "plastic" materials, which polymerize when heat and pressure are applied to them and form bonds that are indissoluble (see Plates XVI and XVII). Laminated veneers, usually called plywood, have leaped into prominence not only in the aircraft industry but in the manufacture of radio cabinets, luggage, small boats, wall board, and dozens of other useful articles. Indeed, they have rescued wood from the doghouse as an engineering material and placed it in competition with aluminum, magnesium, and steel. This does not mean that older types of glues have by any means been wholly replaced, for they are considerably cheaper than synthetic-resin products and are quite satisfactory for ordinary purposes. But the trend in the most progressive techniques is steadily away from them.

After briefly mentioning the bearing of chemical structure and its colloidal implications on adhesive properties, we shall consider the most important classes of glues individually and attempt to distinguish between them as clearly as possible. This is a difficult, not to say "sticky," field to enter upon, as the mechanism of adhesion is not well understood, and the boundaries of organic chemistry, colloid chemistry, and physical chemistry overlap here with particular obscurity.

The animal glue industry has always been rather backward in its technological aspects in comparison with most others. Methods hallowed by antiquity have been followed, with little attempt at any such scientific development as has characterized the rubber and the petroleum industries, for example. Except for some sporadic experimentation, most of the progress made in quality and manufacturing techniques has been improvised. Trade secrets have been jealously guarded by individual companies and passed along chiefly by word of mouth.

As a starter in our attempt at classification and distinction, it may be asserted that adhesion is characteristically a colloidal phenomenon. Although some adhesives, such as the mixtures of crude rubber and resins used in surgeon's plaster and friction tape, do not contain any solvent, most materials that have the property of stickiness are in some form of colloidal dispersion— the continuous phase of which is either water or organic solvent. The question is, what constitutes the dispersed phase? The differences in this respect, as well as the ways in which these dispersions set up, or "gel," underlie the distinction between one type of adhesive and another. The fact that all organic glues are colloids suggests the one point of similarity between them; but obviously it is not enough to call them colloidal systems and let it go at that, because we have discussed many which are not adhesives by any stretch of the imagination.

In thinking over all the substances which are commonly known and used as adhesives—including starch, rubber, casein, animal and fish glues, and natural and synthetic resins—we are forced to conclude that they have only one feature in common: that of being composed of large, complex molecules of the type earlier described as macromolecules. Since proteins are substances of this nature, it is not surprising to find that many adhesives are colloidal suspensions of various proteins in water. This group includes glues made by boiling and soaking the hides, bones, and tendons of animals and fish. By origin, such adhesives as blood albumin and casein are animal proteins. Also belonging to this group are glues derived from various forms of vegetable life rich in proteins, such as soybeans and even peanuts.

But other complex molecules besides those of protein substances have adhesive properties. Let us take starch as an example, as it affords some interesting observations and displays a unique type of gelling action. Starch is not a particularly effective gluing agent, and its commercial use for this purpose is limited to the sizing or coating of paper and various textile products, and the manufacture of the common garden variety of library paste. The chief chemical difference between starches and proteins is that starches are composed of only the elements carbon, hydrogen, and oxygen (for which reason they are called *carbohydrates*), whereas proteins contain nitrogen and usually sulphur as well. Starch, which is also called dextrin, is a close chemical relative of cellulose, or plant fiber, on one hand, and sugar on the other. The closeness of this relationship is brought out by the fact that in some fruits, such as bananas, the ripening process is merely the breaking down of the more complex starches to the simpler sugars. Starch is an almost universal component of growing plants and is especially plentiful in rice, tapioca, potatoes, corn, and wheat.

In the brief description of polymerization given earlier, it was pointed out that it is a chemical change involving the union of many small molecules to form large ones (macromolecules), and that it is the basis of the manufacture of many synthetic products, which are generally called plastics. The synthetic-resin adhesives are formed in this way. But it was also mentioned that starches and proteins are typical of a group of substances that occur in polymerized form *in nature*—that is, the small molecules have already been united into complex chains and rod-like structures. If this is true it would be natural to ask, How are the size and weight of the simple molecule determined, and just how large do the polymerized molecules become?

The answer to the first query may be suggested in this rather crude analogy. Suppose you are looking at a wall covered with paper having a distinct pattern. It is obvious at a glance that the pattern is constantly repeating itself, yet it takes careful examination to say just where the lines of demarcation between the repetitions lie. None the less, it would be quite possible to mark off or isolate what we may call the pattern theme of the paper—a unit which by mere multiplication of itself constitutes the entire pattern. Perhaps it would be an area about a foot square.

Now getting back to the natural polymer starch, the best that chemists can do to express it is to state its basic chemical unit, which corresponds to the pattern theme of the wallpaper, and indicate that this unit is repeated an unknown number of times in the long-chain starch molecule. So the formula is written:

$$(C_6H_{10}O_5)_x$$

meaning that the carbohydrate unit, which has a molecular weight of 162, occurs x number of times in the polymerized macromolecule. The total weight of one of these molecules has not been definitely determined, any more than we could determine exactly the number of repetitions of the pattern theme in a room the size of a convention hall. Obviously it can be represented by $162x$, and the value of x is thought to be about 1000. Thus it can be assumed that the starch molecule probably has a molecular weight in the vicinity of 160,000. For this reason, starches, proteins, and related materials are known as "high molecular weight polymers," or in chemical jargon simply as "high polymers."

The total length of the chains is not accurately known, but that of the base unit can be measured by x-ray diagrams. This unit length, again corresponding to the pattern theme of the wallpaper, is technically referred to as the "identity period" of the substance. It may vary from one to ten millimicrons.

Only one qualification need be made of the statement that adhesive materials are all high polymers. It seems that this is true only if the chains are not *too* long nor the structures *too* big—that is, there is a point between the simple carbohydrate molecule of sugar ($C_{12}H_{22}O_{11}$) and the very complex one of cellulose ($C_6H_{10}O_5)_{x+y}$ at which maximum stickiness occurs. Starch stands about mid-way in complexity between these two extremes. Sugar is slightly sticky, but cellulose is not. This fact is borne out by the behavior of rubber, another natural high polymer substance. When smoked and dried, rubber is not very sticky; but when the long hydrocarbon chains are broken down to simpler molecules by oxidation, a semi-permanent but tenacious adhesiveness sets in. This property is utilized commercially in the manufacture of insulating and surgeon's tape from unvulcanized rubber, with the aid of a little resin or liquid asphalt.

Returning to colloidal considerations, exactly what is the dispersed phase in a system made up of starch and water? It is composed of macromolecules, represented roughly by the approximate chemical formula of starch, and existing in the form of rods or chains. These are analogous to protein macromolecules, though some of the latter occur in round or plate-like structures instead of rods. Consequently, a suspension of such polymers in water constitutes a true colloidal system, even though the dispersed particles are technically molecules. Proteins tend to hold water more effectively than do starches; this is probably a contributing reason why animal and vegetable glues are superior to paste in strength and tenacity. There is by no means complete agreement among scientists as to the exact structure of starch and the means by which it forms a sticky, gelatinous mass when dissolved in water. The explanation which follows is probably as satisfactory as any that has been suggested.

A particle of starch is believed to consist of a central core of a water-soluble substance called amylose, which is encased in a film of amylopectin. This exterior husk is not soluble in water, but it does allow water to seep through it. When dry starch is mixed with water and allowed to stand, the water gradually penetrates the coating of amylopectin. As a result, the interior of the particle swells, and eventually the coating bursts, allowing the amylose molecules to form a colloidal suspension. According to one of the more probable theories, the volume of the continuous phase is slowly reduced as the water evaporates, and the rod-like molecules, which are in constant motion, become crowded together more and more. This causes the solution to thicken. As evaporation continues, the molecules eventually become entangled with one another and are no longer able to move about freely. As a result, they trap droplets of water in the network. When this point is reached, the solution is said to have "gelled" to a stiff paste. It is this characteristic that makes starch useful in laundering. Further evaporation of water takes place very slowly, the imprisoned droplets being unable to escape from the meshes formed by the interlocking molecules. Finally, however, they do evaporate completely and the starch once more becomes a dry powder.

Many colloidal systems form such gels upon evaporation of their continuous phase, but the properties of the gels differ somewhat with the nature of the suspended substance. Starch, gelatin, and egg-white all thicken after standing exposed to the air; and they all have considerable stiffening power, which is utilized in such preparations as meringues, puddings, and cream fillings, to impart body and "richness." Gelatin and egg albumin are "water-loving" materials, but the films of water which they bind to their particle surfaces evaporate much more slowly than does water in the usual free state. Eventually it will evaporate completely, leaving a colorless solid—the form in which gelatin is usually sold.

It is easily possible to add water to this dry material and turn it back into its original colloidally dissolved condition. Egg-white becomes viscous after standing for a few hours, and finally sets to a brittle solid. If water is then mixed with it, and time enough is allowed for the albumin particles to pick it up, the white resumes its original consistency. Both starch and gelatin behave similarly. As previously mentioned, gels which can be restored to their liquid form after drying are termed "reversible;" those which cannot are said to be "irreversible." This is an important distinction, which underlies much of that portion of colloid chemistry involved in water-soluble materials of high molecular weight.

Not all of them behave alike under identical treatment, however. The three just referred to give gels of the reversible type as their continuous phase evaporates; but this is not true when heat is the gelling agency. When gelatin and starch gels are heated they become thinner, and resume their viscous condition on cooling. In short, they are reversible in respect to heat. Egg albumin, on the other hand, though reversible to evaporation, coagulates to a firm, solid mass when heated, and can never be restored to its former fluidity, as everyone knows who has fried an egg. We say, then, that egg-white is irreversible to heat. The same is true of the albumin in milk.

In the case of many of the more important synthetic-resin adhesives, the "setting" or gel formation is caused by artificial polymerization, which is often promoted by a catalyst and heat. This is especially true of the glues used in plywood manufacture. Here the man-made synthetic molecules constitute the dispersed phase of the system. For commercial use they are prepared in the form of fine powders, which quickly dissolve in a little water. Under the influence of the catalyst, the large molecules are chemically united to form a hard, irreversible product which resists attack by acids and alkalies and is extremely strong. It is evident that the chief difference between the starch-protein type of adhesive and the synthetic-resin types just described is in their method of setting; and that this in turn is due to the fact that the former group is made up of *naturally* polymerized molecules which are only *mechanically* united by evaporation of the continuous phase, whereas the molecules of the latter group undergo *chemical* union.

There are certain other kinds of high polymers like rubber which can be colloidally suspended in organic solvents. Here again the gelling action is due to evaporation of the continuous phase and is reversible. A well-known synthetic adhesive of this type is polyvinyl acetate. Ordinary uncured rubber dissolved in naphtha is a most useful "glue" for scrapbook purposes; not only is it extremely tenacious in the liquid state, but the film dries rapidly as soon as the solvent evaporates. This is most convenient when an excess is accidentally used, as the overflow can be readily wiped away without making an unsightly mess on the paper.

In spite of the many advantages of synthetic over protein adhesives, the older types have a wide variety of commercial uses which synthetics do not. For example, animal and vegetable glues are cheap and effective sizing materials for rayon, cotton, and silk fibers, and as an ingredient in coatings for all kinds of paper. Vegetable glues are used in various types of "sticking" uses, such as envelopes and stamps. Animal glue has important properties as a protective colloid, and is sometimes added to rubber latex as an aid in creaming. A unique use is in the manufacture of printing rollers; in combination with glycerin its gelling properties give a soft, pliable surface well adapted for ink transfer. This product, named "Gluglis," is widely used not only in printing but in textile finishing and general coating of materials. Glue is also a component of the heads of matches. It blends readily with such substances as cork, clay, and sawdust, and this property has made it indispensable in composition flooring, shoe soles, gaskets, and similar products.

The specific protein characteristic of the glue obtained from animal hides and tendons has a name with a familiar ring—collagen, which means "glue-maker." Collagen is found in the connective tissue of all animals, and it is extracted by steeping the hides in large tanks for a number of hours. The collagen is separated by filtration after cooling. Gelatin is made in exactly the same way, except that the starting material must be much more carefully selected in view of the use of gelatin in foods.

Again we may emphasize the large size and high weight of the protein molecule. The chemical formula of collagen is $C_{102}H_{149}N_{31}O_{38}$, which gives a molecular weight close to 2500. The only chemical distinction between it and gelatin is that the latter contains a molecule of water as well. That is, collagen plus water produces gelatin. Animal and fish glues are hydrophilic in nature, and their molecules are stabilized, or "hydrated," by intimately bound layers of water. They set when the continuous phase has evaporated, to form hard but reversible gels. Indeed, gelatin is one of the best illustrations of a protective hydrophilic material, as it holds many times its weight of water in this surface-bound condition. Just as collagen is a useful protective colloid in latex, so gelatin is in ice-cream mixes and other food products prepared in emulsified form.

Two great weaknesses of both animal and vegetable

glues are, first, their lack of resistance to water absorption, and second, the fact that they provide a pleasant meal for rodents, moths, and bacteria. It is risky to use casein-laminated plywood in any buildings that are not absolutely squirrel- and mouse-free; otherwise the walls will have some impromptu decoration. Books may be chewed to pieces by glue-hungry rats. Moisture absorption cannot be tolerated in any structure which is required to maintain absolute uniformity of size. This limitation more than any other prevents the use of casein or animal glues in airplane assemblies, for the expansion and shrinkage that result from sudden changes of humidity in the atmosphere are highly undesirable. However, if kept dry and clean, all types of protein adhesives have excellent and permanent bonding properties.

One type of industrially important adhesive of which no mention has been made is liquid sodium silicate, popularly known as "water glass." Because of the abnormal ability of the molecule of this compound to hold water in chemical union and thus to form a thick, colorless liquid, it must be classed as an adhesive even though it is not an organic material. It has the highly useful property of being extremely heat-resistant, which results in its use as a cementing agent in installing furnace linings of firebrick. It is also applied in the manufacture of fiber-board cartons and other coarse paper laminates.

CHAPTER 11

The Importance of Surface

○   ○

○

I T IS NOT AT ALL difficult to see why colloid chemistry has often been called "the chemistry of surfaces," for if a solid or a liquid is divided into smaller and smaller fragments, the *total area* of the surface rapidly increases. As said earlier, a block of wood measuring one foot in each dimension has six sides, each of which is one square foot in area; if cut up into 1728 one-inch cubes, this same block would present a total exposed area of approximately 70 square feet. Now, if the one-inch cubes were still further reduced in size, say to one quarter-inch bits, the surface area would jump to 288 square feet. What area would be covered by the fine-ground sawdust produced from the one-foot cube of wood? It would very likely be in the neighborhood of half an acre, or about 20,000 square feet. Yet we are still in the optical size range!

There are many instances in daily life where surface area on the optical size level is used to advantage. Steam and refrigerator pipes are always built in coils or banks when it is necessary to heat or cool a space of limited volume. The ordinary radiator is a common example; though the dimensions depend on the cubic content of air in the room, a typical radiator consists of ten coils three feet high, which provides the equivalent

155

heating area of a pipe 60 feet long. In cooling milk after pasteurization, a bank of cold-water pipes is used; as the milk cascades over these, virtually all of it at some point comes into contact with the cool surface of one pipe or another. Though these instances are almost too obvious to need mention, the vast importance of contact area in both physics and chemistry can hardly be overstated: the rate, or efficiency, with which one substance reacts with another or with the forces surrounding it depends directly upon the size and shape of its particles—which means, of course, upon the extent of its total surface area.

To get down to colloidal dimensions, it has been found by use of the electron microscope that a single pound of carbon black would blanket an area of no less than *twelve acres* if the surface of all its particles were spread out flat. In like manner, the surface area of a liquid is vastly greater when it is converted into an "atomized" spray than when in the form of large drops. By their very nature, then, all colloidal substances have a tremendous extent of exposed surface, which must be considered to include all the humps, angles, projections, and other irregularities. The total area is often referred to as "active" surface, because the substance is free to react at its exposed points to external influences brought to bear upon it. Powders of colloidal size are highly "surface-active." The significance of this fact for such phenomena as emulsification, reinforcement, and catalysis is definitely of the first magnitude.

The significance of surface area may be brought home by one or two practical examples. Every good automobile tire tread contains about 50 per cent of carbon black. Assuming that the tread alone weighs ten pounds, the total area of the black dispersed in the rubber would be more than fifty acres—over half a million square feet. As the strength and wear resistance of a tire depend on close association between the carbon black and the rubber particles, the importance of this huge area of active surface is obvious.

Dyes owe their strong coloring power in part to their colloidal nature—that is, to their high surface area. It has been reported that a teaspoonful of an aniline dye dropped into the Hudson River at Albany was detected as far south as the George Washington bridge—a distance of 150 miles. Though the identification was undoubtedly made by a colorimeter and would not have been possible to the naked eye, it is none the less amazing that such extreme dispersion was detectable even by an instrument. This phenomenon was put to practical use during the war by equipping lifeboats and emergency rafts with small quantities of dyes of distinctive color. When thrown overboard they so stain the entire area that the location of the boat or raft can easily be spotted from an airplane. Again we may credit Shakespeare with being an unusually keen observer of nature when he had Macbeth observe that his bloody hands "would the multitudinous seas incarnadine, making the green one red."

However, it is not implied that *any* colloidal substance enjoys this coloring power; more is involved than just the surface area. Dyes have a distinctive natural property of reflecting only specific color wavelengths. This is merely intensified by fine particle size.

Since it is so highly desirable to prepare materials of extremely small particle size and large surface area for use in many technological processes, it is not surprising to find that an entire science has grown up around this problem, which is technically called *comminution*. Some materials like carbon black and certain kinds of dyes naturally take the colloidal form and are therefore highly effective coloring agents. Other products, however, must be mechanically comminuted until extremely small particle dimensions are reached. By appropriate devices it is now possible to grind such materials as clays, zinc oxide, sulphur, and dry colors down to particles one micron or less in diameter. One such grinding technique involves the use of a rotating chamber filled with spherical pebbles or balls, which are covered with water. The material to be ground—for example, sulphur—is added to the water, and the unit is given a slow, continuous rotating motion. The friction of the pebbles against the sulphur particles, if maintained for a considerable time, reduces their size to such an extent that if a single drop of the sulphur-water mixture is taken from the churn and placed in a glass of water, the whitish cloud of sulphur particles spreads out and completely obscures the entire volume of water in the tumbler. If the grinding action has gone on for only a short time the particles will eventually fall to the bottom; but longer grinding makes them so small that they will remain in permanent suspension—a true indication that the colloidal size has been attained.

Another method of producing colloids artificially is to blow the material through a pipe or tunnel with a strong blast of air or steam. The friction of one particle on another in transit is so great that sizes of considerably less than one micron are obtained. It is said that the chief drawback of this method is the fact that it is almost impossible to catch the particles as they emerge from the air blast, because they pass through every type of retaining device which contains pores larger than a micron in diameter.

The particles of solid materials vary greatly in their *shape*. Some, like carbon black, appear in the electron microscope as quite spherical and fairly smooth; but in general the tendency in other materials is toward rough, jagged contours, which of course greatly increase the total exposed surface. Cosmetics contain such ingredients as talc and rouge, the particles of which are extremely irregular in shape. Various metallic powders have distinctive shapes and patterns, running the whole gamut from spheres through cubes and tetrahedrons, to long, thin rods and cones. The geometry of nature is indeed a fascinating subject for observation.

It is not the purpose of such a sketchy survey as this to do more than touch upon some of the complex theoretical problems involved in the query, Why is colloidal size so effective in physical and chemical reactions? Leading scientists have long been wrestling with the innumerable aspects of this question that crop up in so many practical industrial processes. A partial explanation may be found in the fact that the surfaces of colloidal particles develop forces, most of which are electrical in nature, which seem to have a profound effect upon the course of events in their immediate vicinity. The smaller the particles, the stronger these forces become. The particle should not be considered simply as a particle, but rather as intimately related to the molecules or particles of the surrounding medium. It is in the boundary area of contact between the surface of one particle and that of another that the critically important forces act. This area is generally termed an *interface*, and the mutual forces exerted are known to scientists as *interfacial* or *surface tension*. This state of affairs is perhaps crudely analogous to the boundary tension between small countries; it sometimes seems that the smaller the country, the more likelihood there is of activity at the frontiers.

Emphasis must again be laid on the fact that the behavior of matter in colloidal form is quite different from that of matter in the larger size ranges. Because of the extreme minuteness of colloidal particles, forces come into play which are negligible at normal dimensions. The surface of such a particle is a dynamic, not a static factor. It is alive and fairly bristling with energy. It exerts a measurable force and exhibits a type of adhesion which is much more like magnetic or electrical attraction than like mechanical "stickiness." The strength of such invisible bonds is sometimes remarkable.

In the case of carbon black dispersed in rubber, as seen in the electron micrograph of Plate XVIII, the black diffuses through the soft, plastic rubber in much the same manner that colloidal sulphur diffuses in a glass of water. After thorough mixing, we have a system comprised of particles of black separated from one another by a network of rubber which itself approaches colloidal thickness (Figure 21). Since rubber is a natural polymer made up of complex macromolecules, these

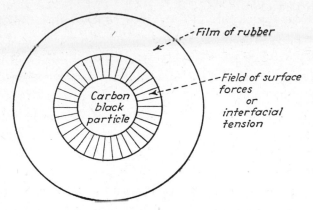

Fig. 21 *An attempt to visualize the surface-active forces in a mixture of rubber and carbon black. The area of the field of force at the interface has been intentionally exaggerated.*

particles exert surface forces; and so do the particles of black. The result is that these minute but relatively potent surface attractions are at work throughout the entire network. Collectively they set up sufficient internal force to bind the system together much more strongly than the rubber alone would be able to do. The bond formed at the rubber-carbon black interface is stronger than that existing between two particles of rubber; hence the reinforcing effect of carbon black.

It has been found that this is even more pronounced in synthetic than in natural rubber. Though the mechanism is probably different, it is none the less true that synthetic rubber would be virtually useless in tires if it were not for the addition of very large amounts of black. A great deal of important research has been carried out on this problem, and it is by no means solved as yet. To summarize this situation in terms of tire wear under normal operating conditions, a natural rubber tread without carbon black might give from 8000 to 10,000 miles of service; with a high percentage of black, from 40,000 to 50,000 miles may be expected. Treads made entirely of Buna-S with plenty of black under the same conditions might run from 30,000 to 40,000 miles; but without any carbon black their performance would probably be limited to a few trips from Westchester to Radio City.

What has been said about carbon black should not be interpreted to imply that *any* substance of equivalent surface area would give the same results in rubber. Nature is more subtle than that. After all, carbon is one of the most chemically active elements; it longs to combine with other elements, especially hydrogen, sulphur, and oxygen. This underscores the futility of trying to consider chemistry and physics in separate categories. The rubber-carbon black situation shows how closely the two are related and how such problems give rise to the science of *physical chemistry.*

It was stated in the opening chapter that a surface irregularity or even a hole can be of colloidal size. This is no matter of idle theory, for use of this fact has saved countless lives by the protection afforded by gas masks. It is also brought into play for the useful purposes of removing objectionable odors and moisture from the air, and discoloring impurities from sugar. This is accomplished by means of a special form of charcoal, prepared by burning cocoanut shells, distilling the resulting charcoal, and then passing steam through it at a very high temperature. This product is made commercially and is known as "activated charcoal." The porous structure presents an extremely large interior area of active surface to the air or other gases which pass through or over it. It is essentially the reverse of the solid-in-solid suspension represented by carbon black and rubber. In effect, it is a gas-in-solid system.

The point to be borne in mind is that here again it is the forces at work at the exposed surfaces inside the mass of charcoal that makes such colloidally porous materials so valuable. As air containing molecules of impurities—such as poisonous gases, odors, or bacteria —filters through a piece of activated charcoal, its surface forces are strong enough to snare and hold tenaciously all or most of them, and permanently remove them from the air. The effectiveness of this treatment is evident from the fact that a standard quantity of ordinary, non-porous charcoal will remove the poisonous gas component from a test mixture for only two minutes, whereas the activated, or colloidally perforated, material will continue to remove it for upwards of thirty-five minutes. In other words, the activated form of charcoal is over seventeen times as efficient as the normal, due to its extremely high internal surface area, which may amount to approximately 3600 square feet per gram, or about 40 acres per pound.

In the canister of a gas-mask is a small amount of such a surface-active material, which picks up the particles of offending or toxic vapors, allowing the purified and de-contaminated air to pass through. The tendency of a porous or finely divided substance to attract and hold such impurities is called its *adsorptive power*. The word "adsorption" means the retention of a molecule or particle of one substance by the active surface of another. Adsorption is an extremely common phenomenon in chemistry. One of its peculiarities is its selectivity, by which is meant the distinct preference which a given surface seems to show for different types of impurities. For example, activated carbon may be much more efficient in retaining molecules of the poison gas chloropicrin than those of water vapor or carbon tetrachloride. In this case it is said to exert *preferential adsorption* on the chloropicrin.

The ability of charcoal or lampblack to pick up moisture by adsorption must have been known, or perhaps was intuitively sensed by the poet Coleridge, for he made the Ancient Mariner exclaim, in describing the tortures of thirst:

> *We could not speak no more than we*
> *Had been choked with soot.*

It is hard to imagine a more effective way of drying up all the saliva which lubricates the mouth and throat than by taking a tablespoonful of chimney black.

Other materials than carbon can be prepared in this porous or surface-active form. One of the best known of these is silica gel, which is an excellent dehydrating agent. It finds wide use in air-conditioning equipment, and in recovering benzene or other solvent vapors in industrial operations. In packet form it is placed in cartons of food products and the like, in which the humidity must be kept constant for a long period. Such highly adsorptive products as activated charcoal and silica gel are also used to remove colloidally suspended colors from water, sugar, and other materials which must be purified.

One application of the principle of adsorption is often unwittingly made by those housewives who still prefer the old-fashioned open coffee pot. It is conventional practice to drop a couple of eggshells into the liquid before boiling—not for any effect that the shells themselves will have, but for the clarifying action of the albumin particles in the egg-white which clings to them. The protein molecules adsorb many of the colloidally suspended impurities which cloud the coffee.

Another and considerably more important instance of adsorptive forces exerted at the surface of fine particles is afforded by the growth of plants and vegetation. One reason why water is essential for growth is that the elements which the plants require must be dissolved in water before the roots can utilize them. No matter how rich the soil may be, or how well fertilized, the nutrient material does the plant no good whatsoever unless it is in water solution. As explained earlier, this means that the various minerals must be present in the form of ions. What happens is something like this. When water enters a dry, finely powdered soil, the mineral compounds which are there in a dry state at once ionize and form a true solution. Each tiny soil particle, irregular in shape, adsorbs a thin film of the nutrient water solution. Air spaces between the particles leave ample room for the watery film. Many of these films, of course, come into contact with the root system of the plant—the surface area of which is itself surprisingly large. As a result, the solution adsorbed on the soil particle is able to diffuse into the cells of the root hairs, and thence from one cell to another throughout the plant. Here is a definite case in which colloidal

phenomena play a dominant part in the story of life—
for without vegetation all life on earth would cease.

Thus far in this chapter the importance of particle
size, of greatly extended surface area, and of the minute
but highly effective forces exerted at surfaces and interfaces has been emphasized almost to weariness—because
it is certainly one of the key facts relating to colloid
chemistry. Without a firm grasp of this truth—and
those who are not in the class of specialists will have to
accept it largely on faith—there can be no real appre-
ciation of the far-reaching significance of the colloidal
state of matter, not only in vital industrial processes,
but in the still mysterious sequence of events which we
know as life and growth. We have now to consider one
of the basic phenomena of all science as it applies to
things which modern man lives with and by. A later
chapter will be devoted to its role in life itself. This phenomenon is *catalysis;* and it is intimately related to and
dependent on the surface-active forces on colloidal
particles.

The most effective and widely employed industrial
catalysts are finely pulverized metals or metallic oxides.
The reason for this will be suggested presently; but at
the moment we at least know that metals so prepared
would have a large area of active surface. The more
commonly used metallic catalysts are aluminum chloride, copper, nickel, platinum, chromic oxide, iron
oxide, silver, manganese dioxide, and vanadium pentoxide. For commercial use these substances are often
supported on a layer of clay or similar inert material,
called a carrier. The catalyst may be either placed in

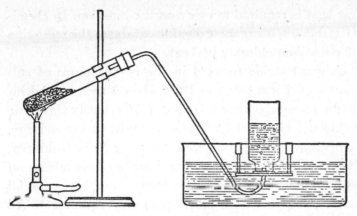

FIG. 22 *Laboratory set-up for producing oxygen from potassium chlorate and manganese dioxide by means of heat applied to the mixture. Note the bubbles of oxygen rising through the water in the inverted container at right.*

the reacting vessel or chamber on its bed of carrier, or blown through the chamber in its pure state. Though our interest is less with the method of application than with the nature of the phenomenon, a few examples of the practical use of catalysts may be informative.

A standard laboratory experiment in first-year chemistry involves heating some potassium chlorate and observing the rate at which oxygen is given off. The oxygen passes through a glass tube and reveals its presence by bubbling into a container of water at the exit end of the tube, as shown in Figure 22. A very slow evolution of oxygen occurs when the potassium chlorate is heated all by itself; only a slight bubbling can be detected in the water. But if a pinch of manganese dioxide is added and the heating is resumed, the rate of oxygen release is so rapid that the water bubbles furiously. Moreover, less heat is required to carry on the reaction. In chemical parlance, manganese dioxide catalyzes the reduction of potassium chlorate by heat.

A great stride forward in the manufacture of sulphuric acid was taken in 1926 when a new method involving a catalyst was introduced. Previously this basic industrial chemical had been made by using a large, complicated installation reminiscent of Rube Goldberg. It comprised no less than five lead-lined chambers, an equal number of intermediate towers, and three special towers, together with much accessory equipment. All this expensive and bulky set-up was required in order to oxidize sulphur dioxide to sulphur trioxide (a very unstable compound) in such a way that it would "stay put" long enough to combine with water to make the familiar H_2SO_4. The essential chemical reaction is:

$$2 SO_2 + O_2 \longrightarrow 2 SO_3 + 2 H_2O \longrightarrow 2(H_2SO_4)$$

| sulphur | oxy- | sulphur | water | sulphuric |
| dioxide | gen | trioxide | | acid |

This reaction will proceed very much more rapidly and efficiently—and without the lead-lined chambers—by passing the sulphur dioxide gas, in the presence of oxygen, over a catalyst mass comprised of vanadium pentoxide and an inert carrier. Since the molecules of the gas filter through the catalyst and thus come into intimate contact with the surfaces of its particles, this method is called the "contact process." So successful and economical has it become that it is well on the way to displacing the chamber process in the United States. The chemical reaction is the same as before; the catalyst does not combine with any of the substances, but merely increases the speed and efficiency of the process.

In the field of petroleum technology—which should be dear to the heart of the gasoline-loving public—a comparably important advance was registered about ten years ago with the introduction of the Houdry catalytic cracking method of producing high-octane motor fuels (see Plate I). "Cracking" of crude oil is a complicated reaction, the general purpose of which is to break down the complex organic compounds occurring in petroleum to relatively simple forms which can be utilized with the highest possible efficiency in airplane and automobile engines. This can be accomplished by a number of cumbersome methods involving very high temperatures and pressures as well as considerable time. In general this is known as thermal cracking, since it relies chiefly on heat. In the Houdry process the cracking is performed much more effectively. The crude oil comes into contact with a synthetic catalyst consisting of pellets of activated aluminum silicate at about 850°F. This does the trick in jig time. Besides giving a superior product, this method has many technical advantages, which have made the thermal process obsolescent. Our high-octane aviation fuel, which helped so much in winning the war, was largely due to this catalytic cracking technique. Other methods of treating petroleum utilize pulverized nickel, tungsten, and molybdenum as catalysts.

Just one more example of industrial catalysis, this time in the food industry. It has long been known from a study of the chemical composition of fats and oils that there is no essential difference between the two except that of consistency—at room temperature a fat is semi-solid and an oil is fluid. It is also known that the hard fats contain much more hydrogen than the fluid oils. Otherwise they are chemically identical. Would it be possible to convert an oil into a fat for cooking purposes by inducing hydrogen to combine with a vegetable oil such as cottonseed? If so, would such a product be salable in competition with lard? The answer to both questions can be found in the popularity of Crisco,* Spry,† and similar products. To make them, finely powdered nickel is added to the oil and hydrogen is then blown through the mixture at a moderately high temperature. The hydrogen molecules unite chemically with the fatty acid molecules of the oil, and thus turn it into a white substance of fat-like consistency. This process is called catalytic hydrogenation. It is also applied to fish and animal oils. For some reason, nickel is almost invariably used. Palladium works still better, but it is prohibitively expensive.

The purpose of describing these instances of catalysis, aside from their intrinsic interest, is to drive home the colloidal significance of this basic phenomenon. Here are the factors which should be remembered:

1. The most effective industrial catalysts are metallic powders.

2. An almost unbelievably small quantity of catalyst is needed in proportion to the amount of product formed.

3. The effect of the catalyst is to accelerate a chemi-

* Product of Procter and Gamble Company, Cincinnati, Ohio.
† Product of Lever Brothers Company, Cambridge, Massachusetts.

cal reaction greatly, and to enable it to proceed at comparatively low temperatures and pressures.

4. The catalyst itself is almost wholly unaffected by the reacting compounds. It may eventually become fouled or poisoned by contaminants, but can be regenerated and used again with little difficulty.

The explanation of the mechanism responsible for catalytic action has provided a fertile field for scientific theorists. It is not possible to say definitely even today that the question has been wholly answered. The word "catalysis" is now over a century old; it was coined by the Swedish chemist Berzelius in 1836. He showed a truly astounding comprehension of what goes on at the interface between a catalyst particle and the molecule of a compound in contact with it. He recognized it as a force capable of bringing about the decomposition of substances, and regarded it as a new manifestation of the well-known forces of chemical affinity which hold atoms together in a molecule. This force is unquestionably electrical in nature, yet it differs in its mode of action from the intermolecular binding forces which are chemically called "valence."

In the case of pulverized metals, it seems that active centers are created at numerous points on the surface by groups of atoms which stick out all over it, much as the heads of old-fashioned pins would protrude from a pincushion after the metal portion of the pin had been inserted to varying depths (as suggested in Figure 23). The activity at these points on the particle is sufficient to induce a corresponding distortion in the surfaces of the molecules in contact with it. In this state of mutual "surface distortion" the contacting substances are

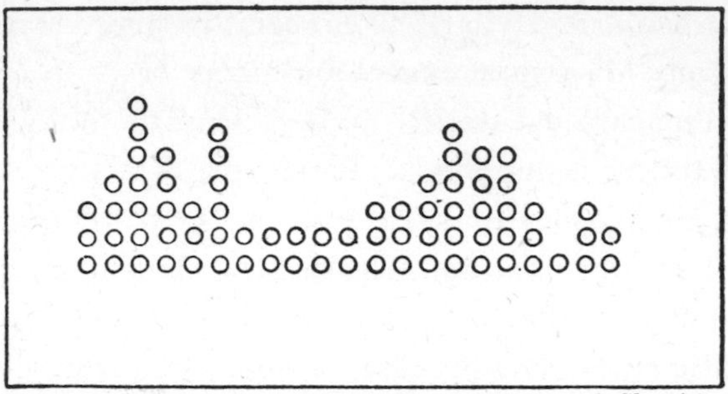

From Riegel: *Industrial Chemistry*

Fig. 23   *The surface of metallic nickel, greatly enlarged to show the catalytically active centers.*

much more likely to react than when in their normal
condition.

In fact, to put the situation in common language,
the action of a catalyst is not unlike that of a zipper
key, which fits into metallic recesses and projections
attached to the sides of the material to be closed or
opened, as it passes over them. These represent the
reacting substances. The process is essentially one of
electrical surface reactivity. The catalyst is the "key"
which unlocks chemical reactions as if by magic. To
relate this theory to the specific case of the hydrogenation of cottonseed oil mentioned above, what happens
may be visualized as something like this: as the molecules of fatty acid in the oil and those of the hydrogen
gas introduced into the oil come into contact with the
surface of the nickel catalyst, they are both changed
from a non-reactive to a highly reactive condition. This
change is induced by the electrical forces that exist on
the "rough," distorted nickel particle. In this way the
two substances combine chemically, after which they
move along, to be replaced by other molecules, which

in turn are activated. This process continues until the oil has taken up hydrogen to the extent desired or until it is completely saturated.

It is the surface irregularities of the catalyst that are actually of colloidal size, not the metallic particles themselves. Adsorption undoubtedly plays a part, but after all this is merely a name applied to a specific result of surface activity. To attempt to go deeper into the theory of catalytic action would carry us too far over into the realms of physical chemistry and electrochemistry- which are so easy to slip into in even a superficial discussion of colloid chemistry.

It may seem that the significance of surface activity has been overemphasized in this chapter; yet we have as yet only entered upon the part it plays in the material world. Again it will bear repeating that, to a great extent, *colloid chemistry is surface chemistry.* And catalysis is a truly colloidal phenomenon.

CHAPTER 12

Soaps, Detergents, and Emulsifiers

 ○ ○

○

W E HAVE NOW come far enough along the winding
and repeatedly forking road of colloid chemistry—
most of the forks have been merely pointed out—to
realize that a significant generalization can be drawn
from the division of matter into major size levels. No
complete understanding of what goes on at any one of
these levels can be gained without some knowledge of
the situation in its neighboring levels. To put it another
way, many phenomena taking place in any given size
range—be it ocular, microscopic, colloidal, or molecular
—are due to, or at least affected by, occurrences in the
ranges immediately below or above. We have already
seen that the behavior of certain adhesives of colloidal
size is governed by the action and structure of molecules; and in going further into the discussion of surfaces and interfacial boundaries we shall again have to
descend one step to the strictly molecular level.

There can be no narrow and exclusive interpretation
of science. Any lines of demarcation drawn between one
group or type of substance and another must be regarded as merely a convenient means of segregation for
the purpose of clearer explanation and understanding,
rather than as fixed and rigid divisions. Nature has a
way of confounding all such artificialities; she often

174

interweaves one thing with another in the most distressingly complicated way. This is one reason why scientific research must be so infinitely painstaking, so methodical, and so dispassionate, for only thus can the overlappings and unexpected irregularities be screened out and the basic pattern revealed.

In the descriptions of milk and rubber latex reference was made to the fact that these substances are natural emulsions, or suspensions of colloidal fat or rubber particles in water, and that they are stabilized, or made permanent, by a protective coating of protein. Let us now go a little deeper into the subject of emulsions. The great importance of understanding the principles of emulsification is obvious when we consider the large part it plays in many operations essential to our daily life and well-being. All aspects of washing, laundering, and cleaning in which water is used depend upon it; so does the manufacture of all products involving mixtures of oily or fatty ingredients: oil shampoos, shoe polishes, face creams, lotions, ointments, and pharmaceuticals; so does the preparation of many types of foods, such as salad dressing, mayonnaise, chocolate milk drinks, and ice cream; so does the formulation of paints and varnishes, leather-dressing compounds, floor waxes, and insecticidal sprays. In addition to all these positive applications, it is frequently desirable to know how to get rid of emulsions where they are not wanted. This is an essential problem in the petroleum industry, as will be explained presently.

A true emulsion is a colloidal system of liquid particles dispersed in another liquid—oil droplets in water, for example, or the reverse. It is obvious that such a system, in common with all colloidal suspensions, is discontinuous: at a given point it is either all oil or all water, and is nowhere a true combination of the two. There is only one exception to this statement—the hairline boundary at which the surface of the oil particle touches the surrounding water. It is here that the phenomena which are crucial for the formation of emulsions occur.

But we had better not go too fast. Like most aspects of colloid chemistry, emulsification is a tricky subject, and any one who attempts to explain it is likely to trip over a subtle technicality or two in every paragraph. First, it is desirable now to distinguish between the word "surface" and the more accurate term "interface." In popular language a surface is conceived as being exposed to the air, as the surface of a table or of the sea. It is evident that even this implies an interface, or a boundary, between a solid or a liquid and a gaseous mixture (air). The nature of the rubber-carbon black interface has been mentioned; and this conception of internal surfaces should be applied also to emulsions, wherein the contacting boundaries of the dispersed and continuous phases are all-important.

Now to get down to brass tacks, why is it that oil and water do not mix? Why should there be any interface at all? Why does the oil separate into visible droplets which float around and through the water but refuse to blend with it? Everyone has noticed many manifestations of this diabolical enmity between different types of substances: oil in vinegar is a good example, or water forming drops which roll like marbles off a paraffined or oily surface, such as the proverbial duck's back. One

may correctly guess that such repulsion is due to a
chemical difference between the two substances; but
this explanation hardly goes far enough, for the chemical composition also involves physical properties of an
electromagnetic nature. It may come as a surprise to
many that water, the universally used inorganic solvent,
is outstanding in this respect. It conducts electricity
much better than do oily organic solvents such as benzene, gasoline, and other hydrocarbon fluids. Moreover,
its molecules exert much more attraction upon one
another. The truth of the latter fact can be observed
by partially filling two containers with water and with
gasoline, respectively, and then noting how readily they
slop around when the containers are moved from side to
side. The gasoline moves with considerably greater ease
and rapidity than the water, not only because it is
slightly lighter, but because its internal molecular cohesion is only about half that of water.

It will be readily seen that a water droplet, being
composed of molecules which have a high degree of
mutual attraction, will tend to draw in upon itself,
something like a clenched fist, rather than to spread
out and merge with another liquid. The effect of this inward pull exerted by the molecules at the interior of
the droplet upon those at the exterior, or outer rim, is
to form the equivalent of a film or skin of downward
pressure on its surface. This force is often called "internal pressure" or "surface tension." The latter designation is used when a liquid is actually exposed to
air, in the conventional use of the word surface. Examples of the surface tension of water, resulting in an
apparent skin formation, are matters of everyday ob-

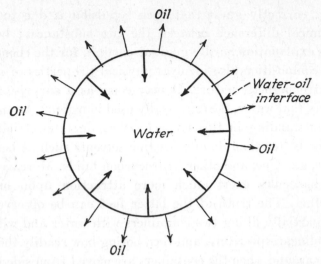

Fig. 24. *Why oil and water do not mix: the molecular forces, indicated by arrows, act in opposite directions when a drop of water is immersed in oil, causing the two liquids to repel each other. The heavy arrows in the water indicate an internal force about twice as strong as that in the oil.*

servation. Spill a pail of it in the street and note the long fingers of water flowing away, each with rounded edges that eventually stop and yet retain their curvature. Or observe the tiny legs of water bugs on a pond or river: though they visibly dent the surface of the water, its "skin" of surface tension is strong enough to afford them support.

The tension caused by the internal molecular attraction of water is quite easily measurable with the proper instruments, and is surprisingly large. The only liquid which greatly exceeds it in this respect is mercury, the surface tension of which is about ten times as high. This accounts for the characteristic crumbling of mercury into pellets when it is spilled on a smooth surface: it simply refuses to flow because of the tremendous inward pull of its atoms. All liquids possess a certain amount of molecular attraction or cohesion; all tend to a greater or less extent to pull away from substances having a lower cohesion value. It is this back pull at the liquid-liquid boundary that constitutes "interfacial tension." It prevents water and oily substances from mixing and makes them mutually repellant.

In recognition of its peculiar properties of molecular attraction, water is known as a *polar* liquid; conversely, oils are called *non-polar* liquids. These words, of course, imply electrical forces, and it will be seen presently how large a part they play in the formation of emulsions.

So far, then, it is clear that, regardless of whether oil droplets are dispersed in water or water droplets in oil, there exists a rather strong tension at the interface which prevents any blending of the two liquids. What can be done to overcome this situation? How can the repelling forces be removed or diminished so that a usable mixture or emulsion is obtained? A temporary means of doing so is to shake the dispersion vigorously. This reduces the size of the droplets somewhat by breaking the interfacial film for the moment. But mechanical agitation is only an expedient. What is desired is a fine, permanent colloidal suspension which can be used for commercial purposes. Evidently something must be added which is able to affect the interfacial tension. But before this can be correctly understood we must determine more exactly the chemical nature of the two phases, oil and water.

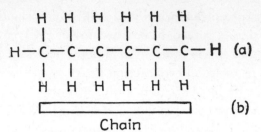

FIG. 25 *Structure of a paraffin oil molecule:*
(a) actual; (b) as visualized.

To keep the discussion as simple as possible let us confine it to the paraffin group. Many oils, of both mineral and vegetable origin, having far more complex compositions, behave similarly. Paraffin oils are pure hydrocarbon liquids derived from certain grades of crude oil and consisting of a series of carbon atoms arranged in straight chains. To each carbon atom are attached two hydrogen atoms. The familiar white solid paraffin is chemically very similiar to these oils, except that it has far more atoms in its molecule, the formula of which is something like $C_{70}H_{142}$. Paraffin may be obtained as a residue after complete distillation of the crude oil. The point to be remembered is that paraffin oils are composed of long strings of CH_2 groups, as shown in Figure 25. As stated above, they have comparatively low interfacial tension, which allows them to flow or spread more freely than water. They are also non-polar and have no pronounced electrical properties. This is in keeping with the meaning of the word "paraffin," derived from the Latin "having very little affinity."

The water molecule, for all its apparent simplicity, is quite different. Though usually written as H_2O, it

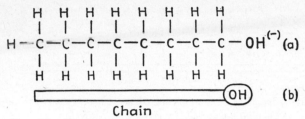

Chain

FIG. 26 *Structure of a molecule of octyl alcohol:*
(a) actual (8–carbon chain, polar head); (b) as visu-
alized.

is more meaningful to consider it as HOH. In this
form it has at least a theoretical resemblance to an
alcohol, since every alcohol molecule ends in an OH
group. The water molecule is strongly polar. The fact
that it can be separated into positive hydrogen ions
(H^+) and negative hydroxyl ions (OH^-) is evidence of
its electrical nature.

In oils and water, then, we have two distinct types
of molecule, as regards both shape and function: the
former a long, slender chain, the latter a hydroxyl
group (OH) associated with a hydrogen atom and
capable of exerting electrical force. The only hope of
overcoming the tension at the interface between such
antagonistic substances seems to lie in some type of
molecule which possesses *both* of these characteristics
—that is, a long hydrocarbon chain on one end and an
electrically charged group of atoms on the other. Such
molecules do exist. They are found among the alcohols
(Figure 26), and also among a class of substances generally called fatty acids. Such acids are derived, as the
name implies, from animal and vegetable fats. The
better known fatty acids are stearic acid, palmitic acid,
and oleic acid. Since stearic acid, which can be con-

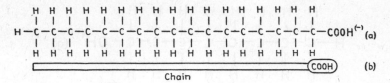

FIG. 27 *Structure of a molecule of stearic acid:* (a) *actual (17–carbon chain and polar head);* (b) *as visualized.*

sidered typical, has the formula $C_{17}H_{35}COOH$, it furnishes a combination of a chain having 17 carbons and 35 hydrogens on one end and the polar COOH group on the other. Such a group is found in all organic acids, and may be visualized as a small circle which forms the "head" of the molecule. The hydrocarbon chain may be represented as a straight line forming the "tail," as indicated in Figure 27. Alcohol molecules also have this arrangement, though they are not as effective as the fatty acids in reducing interfacial tension.

Since fatty acids are the raw materials of soap manufacture, we begin to understand why soap is such an efficient tension breaker and why it helps water in removing grease and dirt. More will be said about the mechanism of the process presently; but we must hasten to point out that there is one important chemical difference between soap and the fatty acids. In making ordinary soap, a fatty acid is reacted with an alkaline metal compound, which is usually caustic soda (NaOH). As a result, the hydrogen atom is displaced from the COOH group by the sodium atom (Na), so that the group becomes COONa. This is still a polar unit, but it is strongly alkaline rather than acidic. Acidity and alkalinity have little bearing upon the question of interfacial tension.

The explanation of the emulsifying action of alcohols and fatty acids presented here is essentially the theory of two well known American scientists who have done outstandingly brilliant work in this field. They are Drs. Irving Langmuir of the General Electric Company and William D. Harkins of the University of Chicago. Their experiments and calculations have been so carefully carried out that their ideas may be regarded as virtually unassailable. Stated very briefly, it is their opinion that, when water and oil are mixed with a small amount of emulsifying agent and the mixture shaken or agitated, each particle of oil becomes coated with a layer of fatty acid or alcohol which is only *one* molecule thick. The polar end of the molecule of the emulsifier (OH or COOH), being negatively charged, is attracted to the positive portion of the water molecule with the result that the emulsifier molecule swings around like a compass needle, coming to rest with its polar "head" in the water and its nonpolar hydrocarbon "tail" in the oil (Figure 28). This pronounced alignment occurs because the head of the molecule is soluble in water, and the tail in oil, in accordance with the general chemical principle that "like dissolves like."

The result of this orientation is to form a monomolecular layer of fatty acid or alcohol molecules at the interface. This layer acts as a sort of bridge or link between the continuous and the dispersed phases, minimizing the discontinuity and making the system as nearly homogeneous as possible. It is generally agreed that the suspended droplets of an emulsion are stabilized by external electrical charges in much the

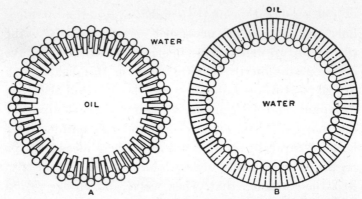

From Berkman and Egloff: *Emulsions and Foams*

F<small>IG.</small> 28　*The Harkins-Langmuir concept of soap molecules aligned at the oil-water interface to form emulsions by lowering surface tension. At left is an oil droplet suspended in water, at right, a water droplet suspended in oil. The type of emulsion formed depends on the chemical nature of the metal attached to the hydrocarbon chain: sodium gives an oil-in-water emulsion (A), as in ordinary soap, whereas calcium and zinc form the water-in-oil type (B).*

same manner as the particles in a colloidal gold solution. Whether the emulsion consists of oil droplets dispersed in water or of water droplets in oil is thought to depend on the type of emulsifier—sodium and potassium soaps giving the former type, and calcium and zinc soaps the latter. Sodium and potassium, being monovalent metals, have only one hydrocarbon chain, or tail, attached to them; but calcium and zinc, which are divalent, can boast two such tails. Here is another case where the shape of a molecule has a significant effect at the colloidal size level.

The statement that fatty acid films have a "thickness" of one molecule is not an exaggeration, but a scientifically demonstrable fact. Drs. Langmuir and

Harkins carried out a long series of investigations on the spreading of such films on a water surface. Under properly controlled conditions, a minute drop of stearic acid placed at one end of a sizable shallow tank of water will gradually move out to cover its entire surface. As it does so, the molecules orient themselves as just explained, with their polar groups sticking down in the water and their tails upward, something like a lot of pollywogs standing on their heads. As the film marches across the water it has sufficient force to push a small paper "boat" before it, which provides an effective demonstration in a lecture room. It is claimed that monomolecular films of fatty acids can be deposited on glass surfaces, where they bring about a notable increase in light transmission.

The interfacial layer of a fatty acid emulsifier is in some respects so similar to the layer of protein which has previously been described as a protective colloid—the protein coating of a rubber latex particle, for example—that an attempt to distinguish between them seems somewhat academic. Both make the transition from oil to water far less abrupt, and result in permanent colloidal dispersions. The chief difference appears to lie in the shape and the electrical properties of the molecules involved. Protein molecules are also polar in nature, yet their structure differs from that of soap molecules. It is undoubtedly true that adsorption forces play a part in forming both types of coating. Protein molecules are extremely fond of attaching themselves to water molecules; as we have seen, it is this striking affinity for water that has earned them the name "hydrophilic." This property fundamentally accounts for their ability to stabilize emulsions. Such protective agents as gum tragacanth and gum arabic are widely used in pharmaceutical preparations, as well as in food products. Gelatin, karaya gum, and sodium alginate, the latter obtained from seaweed, also belong to this group of hydrophilic emulsifying agents. They do not form monomolecular films, however. That seems to be a peculiarity restricted to the fatty acids and alcohols. Without going further into the technicalities, it may be said that there are distinct differences between the hydrophilic and the self-orienting types of emulsifier—that is, between protein-rich substances and fatty acids. To distinguish between them, the latter are usually called *detergents,* because of their relaxing effect on interfacial tension.

Soap, which has been known and used for centuries, is a fairly good detergent. In a sense one might say that it makes water wetter by overcoming the natural repulsion between it and the oily substances which characterize most "dirt." Its universal use as a cleansing agent is due to its ability to emulsify these particles in water; bits of solid matter cling tenaciously to them, and are easily removed by rubbing or wiping. An important and unique industrial application of soap is to stabilize synthetic rubber emulsions, which are analogous to oil-in-water dispersions. Several types of synthetic rubbers pass through a latex stage in which this treatment is used instead of a protective protein.

As previously stated, soap is primarily a fatty substance; yet because one end of its molecule has a strong affinity for water, it is able to establish a "bridgehead" between the mutually repellant grease and water, allowing them to wet each other more effectively. Soap molecules in concentrated water solution are of colloidal size. Such mixtures of soap and water, like starch, gelatin, and other hydrophilic substances, will set to a stiff gel after standing for a time at room temperature. The mass of goo that covers a bar of soap which has been left overnight in a non-draining dish after being used is a common example of this water-holding propensity. However, a slight increase in temperature, or the addition of a little more water, quickly restores the gel to its former fluidity.

Soaps vary greatly in their detergent power, depending on their ingredients. Like most other modern products they are tailor-made to fit specific service conditions. Castile soap, made from olive oil, is designed primarily for infants. Next comes the whole competitive array of toilet and fine laundry soaps guaranteed by romantically inclined advertisers to produce a "skin you love to touch." The harsher, more highly detergent varieties are used for breaking the heavy oils and greases encountered by mechanics and repair men.

Highly useful as it is for ordinary cleansing purposes, soap has several disadvantages when exceptionally delicate or "elegant" results are desired. One of these is its high alkalinity, which causes roughness and cracking of the skin when soapy water is used to excess. The higher-grade toilet soaps are less objectionable, but are far too expensive to use for dishwashing. Another and much more serious drawback is the reaction that occurs between soap and the calcium compounds always present in water to a greater or lesser extent. This reaction causes the formation of insoluble products which are precipitated and cling to any object with which the soapy water is in contact. The best illustration of this is the unpleasant-looking ring that remains in the bathtub. This is not an indication that more frequent bathing is desirable, but merely a deposit of an insoluble calcium-soap complex. No harm is done to either the tub or the body by this precipitate; but when it comes to washing a finely divided material like human hair, it is obvious that such a scummy precipitate would destroy all hope of a lustrous, alluring hair-do.

Ever on the alert to improve their products, leading soap manufacturers have spent much time and money in developing new and more efficient types of detergents which will overcome these two defects of soap. Many successful synthetic detergents for fine laundering and cleansing have been introduced in recent years, and have proved decidedly beneficial. For example, "Duponol" * is designed to eliminate calcium precipitation and provide a better lather in hard water than does ordinary soap. Another, "Drene," † is far superior to soap as a tension breaker in shampooing, and also does away with the dull and unsightly precipitate, leaving each hair clean and smooth (Plate XIX). Moreover, it is not alkaline, but neutral. This detergent is similar to the soap molecule, except that it contains a sulphate group (SO_4Na) instead of the COONa group. It is chemically known as alkyl sulphate, and is made from fatty acids reduced to alcohols, treated with sul-

* Fatty alcohol sulphate. Until recently called "Gardinol." Product of E. I. du Pont de Nemours & Company, Inc., Wilmington, Delaware.

† Product of Procter and Gamble Company, Cincinnati, Ohio.

phuric acid and neutralized. The development of these and many other synthetic substances for breaking interfacial tension and increasing the effectiveness of cleansing processes in many fields has proved a valuable aid to modern civilization, and is typical of the progressive attitude of American industry. It also offers yet another instance of the practical value of colloid chemistry.

A sidelight on the leather industry may be of interest at this point, for it is typical of the application of emulsions during the processing of an industrial product. After raw hides have been tanned, or hardened to make them durable, they undergo a treatment known in the trade as *fatliquoring,* the purpose of which is primarily to impart flexibility and smoothness of texture to the finished material. The necessity for this arises from the fact that the gelatinous nature of the hide fibers would cause them to cohere tightly when dried, and thus to be extremely hard and boardlike. This can be prevented by interposing interfaces of oil between the protein fibers so that they will not unite to form hard, stiff masses. The question is, how to get the oil to penetrate the tiny interstices between the fibers; and the answer is, by means of emulsions.

Numerous oils are used, depending on the grade and finish of the leather. A typical fatliquor consists of an animal oil known as neatsfoot, colloidally dispersed in water by a special type of fatty acid emulsifier made by reacting neatsfoot oil with sulphuric acid. This provides a polar sulphate group which is attracted to the water molecule; the "tail" of the molecule is again a hydrocarbon chain. Sometimes this is converted into a "soap" by the addition of a little borax, which is a compound of sodium (Na). It has been found that the oil penetrates the hide more effectively if a small amount of egg yolk is included in the emulsion. After the fat-liquor has been prepared and the emulsion stabilized, it is placed in a rotating drum with the hides to be treated. After twenty-five or thirty minutes of "tumbling," the oil will have permeated the external layers sufficiently and the skins are removed and dried. Usually the penetration is complete if the skins are fairly thin.

Up to this point we have been discussing desirable emulsions and methods for creating them; but there are cases in which obstinately stable emulsions occur in nature in just the places where they are most annoying. Knowledge of their colloidal behavior has enabled engineers and chemists to devise means of destroying or "breaking" such emulsions—particularly in the petroleum industry, where they are an unmitigated nuisance in both the production and refining of crude oil. The presence of water droplets as a dispersed phase in petroleum deposits may be surprising to those who are not especially familiar with oil-production problems. It is due to the geologic formations in which oil is found, illustrated in Figure 29. Subterranean domes of limestone, often accompanied by rock-salt deposits, are quite likely to contain deposits of crude oil, usually covered by a layer of hydrocarbon gases and resting on a bed of salt water and sand. It is interesting to note that we have here what might be called a petrified ocean: the oil is thought to have originated from the

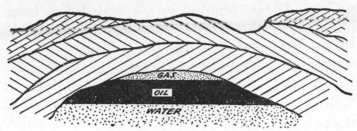

From Kalichevsky: *Amazing Petroleum Industry*

FIG. 29   *Imaginary cross-section of an oil pool. Note the dome-shaped layers of rock and soil.*

bodies of countless billions of tiny marine animals, and the salt and residual brine are all that is left of the sea which covered the oil-bearing region millions of years ago.

The entire deposit of oil, gas, and water is under high pressure inside its integument of limestone. The water is not separated from the oil by a sharp line, as indicated in Figure 49, but is dispersed in it in the form of a water-in-oil emulsion. The emulsifying agents are metallic soaps resulting from the reaction between mineral compounds in the water and organic acids in the oil. Consequently the oil delivered by a producing well is frequently peppered through with water droplets of varying sizes, mostly microscopic and colloidal, which give it a milky cast. Everyone knows the difficulty experienced when water gets into the gas feed line of an automobile. The two substances are incompatible in every way and must be kept apart, for water is ruinous to all forms of petroleum utilization. Indeed, pipeline companies permit a maximum of only 2 per cent of water emulsified with the oil. Crude oil must therefore be "dehydrated" in the field, before being passed on to the refineries. This can be accomplished either by electrical or by chemical treatment.

The electrical method may involve the use of either alternating or direct current. Although both types of current succeed in breaking the water-in-oil emulsion, the two processes are entirely different in principle. When it is desired to remove the suspended water droplets from a quantity of crude oil with alternating current, the emulsion is fed into a tank the shell of which forms one electrode and a set of revolving plates the other. This set-up was devised about forty years ago by the same Dr. Frederick Cottrell who introduced the electrical precipitation of smoke and dust particles. Since an alternating current is continually reversing its direction, its effect on the emulsion is to cause the water droplets to line up between the electrodes something like beads on a string. They eventually approach each other so closely that they unite, or coalesce. When enough of them have thus gotten together they fall to the bottom of the tank by gravity, water being considerably heavier than oil, and the separation is complete.

The direct current dehydrator operates on the principle described in connection with the electrodeposition of rubber latex. It was mentioned that each colloidal particle of an emulsion has an external electrical charge closely associated with it. If a petroleum emulsion is passed between two electrodes less than an inch apart, the charged particles of water will migrate toward the terminal having the opposite charge—that is, the water droplets, which usually carry a negative charge, will flow toward the positive electrode under the influence of the direct current. Here of course they lose their charges and settle out, leaving the oil entirely free from water. To summarize the electric dehydration processes, then, we can say that alternating current causes alignment and coalescence of the droplets; direct current, on the contrary, causes the droplets to travel to the oppositely charged terminal, where they are discharged, following the usual behavior of colloidal particles.

The means by which oil-field emulsions are broken by treatment with chemicals are so many and diverse that we shall not try to describe them in detail. They may be roughly classified into two groups: first, those relying on neutralization of the sustaining electrical charges; second, those which act by counteracting the emulsifying action of the soaps which form the water-oil interface. The first method, as might be presumed from what has been said regarding the purification of water, involves the addition of an acid which will liberate positively charged hydrogen ions to cancel off the negative charges on the water droplets. Both hydrochloric and sulphuric acids have been proved effective for this type of treatment.

In the second technique, substances called demulsifiers are added to the emulsion. They may act in any one of several ways. Some tend to displace the interfacial film already present or to decrease its protective action; others dissolve the metallic soaps of which the film is composed; and still others disrupt it by changing the emulsion from water-in-oil to oil-in-water. The variety of materials and chemicals that have been found to have some degree of effectiveness for demulsification is surprisingly wide, ranging from solvents like benzene and ether to such solid agents as fine clays, silicates, and even powdered glass. A special commercial preparation named Tret-O-Lite * is marketed for this purpose.

The technology of emulsions is complex and the literature voluminous, as is indeed the case with virtually every aspect of colloid chemistry. Perhaps enough has been said to give a bare indication of the nature and the practical importance of these mixtures. It should again be emphasized, however, that some of the explanations attempted in this and in other chapters still have the status of theories. They should not be accepted as literal fact, but merely as the best working hypotheses that have so far been advanced. The entire science of colloid chemistry, being relatively new, is shot through with divergent theories and wide differences of opinion among the most competent scholars. This situation makes the task of simplified explanation extremely hazardous, for an author inevitably lays himself open on every hand to charges of distortion, misguidance, and no doubt ignorance to boot. None the less, an effort has been made to chalk in the rough outlines of this fascinating and highly important subject, the details of which are so multitudinous and abstruse.

With this caution regarding the inexact state of much of the knowledge of colloidal phenomena, we approach the subject of biology, in reference to which the word caution should be doubly underscored.

* Product of the Tret-O-Lite Company, Los Angeles, California.

CHAPTER 13

Colloid Chemistry and Life

○   ○

○

WHAT A PIECE OF WORK is a man! how noble in reason! in apprehension how like a god! the beauty of the world! the paragon of animals! And yet . . . what is this quintessence of dust?" . . . It is a little disillusioning to realize that this famous speech of Hamlet's refers to an organism comprising 75 per cent of water, 5 per cent of mineral elements, and most of the balance protein substance—the whole having a cash value of something less than a dollar. But the disillusionment need not persist. Since the story of life is basically one of structure and arrangement—of how matter is put together—it will be seen that in a very real sense any functioning system involves more than merely the sum of its parts. A piece of machinery requires correct assembly of its units if it is to run properly. The great difference between a biological organism and a machine is that the latter requires an external intelligence, first to conceive it, and then to put it together; while in the case of the organism the "intelligence" is internal. This is merely another way of saying that the organism is alive and the machine is dead. In the marvelous assembly line of nature, what are the guiding and directing agencies? What basic principle activates it? An answer to these questions would help to bring us a little closer to the explanation of life.

To begin with, no life can exist in the absence of proteins. These compounds are found everywhere in the animal and vegetable world, from the very lowest to the topmost level—which is, of course, man himself. An idea of how indispensable they are in vital processes is given by the fact that the word "protein" is derived from the Greek, meaning "first." As all the proteins that exhibit living characteristics are macromolecules, it is undeniably correct to say that life begins at the colloidal size level. Above this level are the more complex forms; below it are the amino acid molecules and their constituent atoms—carbon, nitrogen, oxygen, and hydrogen. Life does not appear in any form of matter until these four elements become united in a molecule, and until this molecule—an amino acid—is in turn united with a vast number of similar structures to form the complex three-dimensional network known as a protein.

If we had to choose four out of the 92 elements and resolve to get along without all the others, it would have to be these, for they are indeed the Big Four of existence. Just to play around with them a bit, we readily see that carbon and hydrogen are the source of coal and petroleum and the vast number of substances derived from them; that oxygen and nitrogen make up the air we breathe; that hydrogen and oxygen comprise life-sustaining water, which makes up three-fourths of the human body; and that nitrogen is the essential growth factor in all soils. Indeed, it is the specific function of plants to get these four elements together.

Amino acid molecules—below the colloidal range in

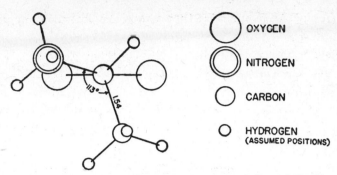

From Cohn and Edsall: *Proteins, Amino Acids, and Peptides*

FIG. 30   *Tho structure of an amino acid molecule.*

size—are the components of the proteins. They may be
visualized as the individual pieces of a jig-saw puzzle,
the complete picture unit being the protein macromolecule. To appreciate the bearing of structure on the
whole problem of biological life, we must step away down
to the level of atoms for a moment. Amino acids are not
haphazard combinations of the four kinds of atoms just
mentioned. Even though their composition is simple, it
is explicit. It consists of a chain of carbon atoms, which
may be long or short depending on the properties of
the compound. On one end of the chain is the now familiar carboxyl group (COOH), which was described
in connection with fatty acid molecules. This makes
that end of the molecule acidic, and gives it a strong
affinity for water. On the opposite end are one nitrogen
and two closely associated hydrogen atoms. This is
called an amino group (NH_2) and it makes that end
of the molecule *basic* (the reverse of acidic). So it is
evident that the specific structure of these Janus-like
substances—the way in which their atoms are assembled
—makes them highly versatile and easily adapted to

different environments: they can react with both acids and bases, and are both water-loving (hydrophilic) and water-hating (hydrophobic).

The amino acids combine with one another by a process analogous to polymerization, the acidic portion of one linking up with the basic portion of another until they eventually become large and complicated enough to constitute a protein molecule—which may contain several thousand amino acid groups, just as a monstrous puzzle might be composed of thousands of small units. As may well be imagined, the number of protein substances is very large and their structures are almost inextricably complex. In extreme cases the total molecular weight of a protein is well up in the millions; in those of average size it runs from twenty to fifty thousand. Yet these structures have been proved to be single molecules, because they are the smallest possible units of those particular substances.

But somehow, somewhere, an amino-acid molecule must have originated independently—the four essential elements had to combine in just the right structural balance. No one knows when or how this occurred, or whether it was pure accident or a specific act of creation. It is the opinion of one authority * that on a basis of mathematical probabilities, it would take a vastly longer time for this union to occur *by chance* than the earth has been in existence. We shall have to assume from the evidence around us that the original amino acids and proteins *were* formed somewhere back in the

* The eminent French biologist, P. Lecomte du Noüy ("Human Destiny," Longmans Green, New York, 1947).

geologic dawn, and that life subsequently made its appearance on this planet.

And what *is* life, indeed? Probably everyone has asked himself that pregnant question many times. Poets, philosophers and scientists alike have sought the answer without complete success. The biologist considers that life is present if two requirements are fulfilled: (1) the organism must be able to grow and to maintain itself in its environment; and (2) it must be able to reproduce itself. Growth, which implies ingestion and excretion of nutrients, and reproduction, may be said to be the most essential criteria of a living unit. As we start with the individual atoms and work upward, we find no such conditions until the protein macromolecule is reached in the lower colloidal range. From there upward, organisms are composed of protein units which become increasingly complex and more and more highly specialized. Man, the climax of all creation, and with all his amazingly intricate systems of digestion, reproduction, and nervous organization, is really one vast protein-water gel, which varies in viscosity and function from point to point, but is none the less a colloidal complex. Every organ in the body except the skeleton is primarily built up of protein substances—skin, muscles, hair, nails, blood, and nerves. The basic constituent of the cells which make up these structures is called protoplasm—a complicated mixture of numerous proteins which enables the cell to grow and reproduce itself.

Perhaps the simplest type of organism in which life exists is the virus. Several viruses have been ob-

served in the electron microscope and are familiar to all
biologists. Those most often studied are the tobacco
mosaic and the tomato bushy stunt viruses. Both have
been found to consist of a single macromolecule, which
has a weight of about ten million. Tobacco mosaic appears as long, narrow rods, as shown in Plate XX.
Bushy stunt is quite different, being spherical in shape.
These giant molecules have been isolated in the ultracentrifuge and chemically purified by crystallization.
The influenza virus has also been observed in the electron microscope. The poliomyelitis virus has not yet
been isolated. But we are speaking here of the place of
the virus in the development of living from inanimate
matter, rather than of its medical importance, great as
that is. Of viruses, Dr. Wendell M. Stanley, one of the
pioneers of research in this field and recent winner of
the Nobel Prize for work in protein chemistry, has
written that they "serve as a bridge between the molecules of the chemist and the organisms of the bacteri-
ologist, and provide us with new reasons for considering that *life, as we know it, owes its existence to
structure*—to a specific state of matter—and that the
vital phenomenon does not occur spontaneously, but is
possessed in varying degrees by all matter." *

This may appear to be a surprising statement—especially the last clause. Reduced to lowest terms, it
simply means that if life is a result of specific structure
—as has been pointed out in the case of the amino acids
—it may be shared to some extent by all substances,
since they all have some kind of structure, no matter
how simple. It implies further what is now the con-

* Italics mine.

sidered opinion of many biologists: that the line of division between living and non-living *is not precise and sharp, but indistinct and hazy;* that there is a twilight zone wherein life may or may not exist, depending on the definition one chooses to apply to the term; and that the difference between animate and inanimate is primarily one of degree of complexity.

However, there are good reasons for believing that the viruses are actually the simplest form of living organism. Perhaps the strongest of these is the presence in the viruses of an active catalytic mechanism. Since this phenomenon of catalysis plays the central role in all life processes, it is of the highest importance that its nature be understood. In a previous chapter catalysts were described as fine metallic powders of irregular surface contour, which are able to accelerate, direct, and even initiate chemical reactions by means of the electromagnetic forces present on their surfaces. This description must now be extended to include molecular protein complexes, many of which behave in a similar way. All of the so-called "miracle" components of the body owe at least a portion of their activity to catalysis —which explains why minute traces of hormone substances, vitamins, and enzymes are able to bring about far-reaching effects on physical peculiarities and personality traits.

There is one great difference in function between the industrially important catalytic materials—all of which are definitely inanimate—and the organic catalysts within the living organism. The products resulting from the former are entirely different from the catalyst itself; but some of the organic catalysts have the unique ability to bring about reactions of which they are themselves the products. This is what goes on in the viruses, which are definitely known to be self-catalyzing and to reproduce themselves in this manner—a phenomenon which is termed *autocatalysis*. No inanimate matter can perform this act of self-perpetuation, which may be tentatively accepted as the really fundamental criterion of life. It is indeed remarkable that the directing influence of catalysis can perform such wonders in both the inanimate and the animate spheres—a fact which underscores the opinion of Dr. Stanley and others that some aspects of life pervade all matter, and that the transition from the non-living to the living state is almost imperceptible.

Before taking leave of the viruses it should be mentioned that, in common with some other proteins, they have external electrical charges, and migrate in an electrical field to the oppositely charged terminal. Much use is made in modern medicine of this property of *electrophoretic mobility*, notably in the study of immunology. Since all the well-known allergies involve responses of the organism to protein-containing substances such as pollen, wool, and even milk, the value of this branch of colloid chemistry to the human race is self-evident.

Though it is customary in standard discussions of biological problems to begin with the cell and its protoplasm, we are approaching the subject from the opposite direction, since the vital colloidal and molecular activity takes place far below the microscopic size range of the cell. Compared to a virus or a protein macromolecule a cell would be the size of a football. It is not only in the cells, but in their protein components and their reproductive mechanism that the really important events occur.

Perhaps the most biologically significant of these components are the genes, which as far as animals and man are concerned, are the smallest living unit. Every cell contains thousands of different genes, all of which have vital duties to perform. These, like the viruses, are autocatalytic and self-perpetuating. Although they are made up of proteins, they are almost certainly not individual molecules. As it is their primary function to guide and control the growth characteristics of the cell, and to pass them along to other cells, the genes are responsible for the transmission of hereditary traits from one generation to another—color of hair, skin and eyes, abilities of various kinds, and other physical and mental characteristics. Genes have never been isolated, and knowledge about them has had to be obtained indirectly; yet it is certain that catalysis is largely responsible for their unique activity.

Biologists are approaching ever nearer to a resolution of the life problem when they study viruses and genes; and it is well worth a moment's pause to emphasize the presently accepted theory, stated by such authorities as Dr. C. R. Plunkett, Jerome Alexander, and others, that areas of catalytic activity exist within these large units which enable them to reproduce themselves. This is due to the presence of fields of force on the surfaces of their component protein aggregates. This phenomenon is not found at any other level of structure, and it sheds a fresh light upon the baffling question of life. It certainly does not provide a definitive answer, though it does suggest the underlying mechanism. Catalysis has doubtless been a major factor in the evolutionary process, initiating gradual changes from lower, less complex, less adaptable species to higher, more complex, more adaptable ones. As biological research progresses, it is becoming increasingly evident that catalysis is the mainspring of all creation.

Even a partial explanation of this amazing process would take us far into the depths of electrochemistry, perhaps even down to the electrons themselves. Its sudden appearance in proteins of extremely high molecular weight may perhaps be explained by regarding catalysis as a function of complexity of organization: as an inanimate protein molecule grows more and more complicated, a point is finally reached at which the scattered, minute surface forces combine, and thus become great enough in very large molecules to initiate reactions which result in splitting off new centers of organization.

There is no essential difference between the small inanimate and the large living units; but there *is* a distinction between the surface activity of the two, and this is indeed the critical consideration. This seems to bear out Dr. Stanley's belief that "the vital phenomenon does not occur spontaneously, but is possessed in varying degrees by all matter." It is also in agreement with the time-honored generalization of biologists that "nature does not make jumps." The comparison of the action of a catalyst to that of a zipper,—the concept of mutual surface distortion induced by electronic forces—is perhaps the best mechanical explanation of this phenomenon that has yet been offered. It is clear that nature is far too intricate to be understood at any one level of structure; and not even the most learned probing of the subatomic forces which play such a large part in all vital phenomena has yet really unveiled the mystery of life.

Just how essential the principle of self-catalysis is becomes clearer when we stop to consider how it happens that a single fertilized cell can develop into a complete new animal, perfect down to the last detail. How is it that, as the cells divide and reproduce themselves, they also take on the specific characteristics of various parts of the anatomy—some being destined to become bone, others muscles, still others nerve—all from the two original cells? What accounts for the differentiation which takes place in cell structure as the new organism gradually develops? It is believed that the unique property of autocatalysis is the primary influence in this specialization of the cells, although the state of chemical and physical activity of the protoplasmic substances also plays a part. It is known that the human embryo passes in various stages through the complete evolutionary cycle. At one point it has gill slits like a fish, at another a rudimentary tail like a pollywog. This remarkable fact led Thomas Henry Huxley to make his characteristically witty remark that before birth "every child has to climb its own ancestral tree." Much of this development is fostered by autocatalytic mechanisms, with able assistance from other growth-promoting agents.

It is not only in the genes and viruses that catalysis is at work. It is closely related to the functions of enzymes, vitamins, and hormones—so closely, in fact, that it is almost impossible to describe the action of any one of these without involving the others. The great difference between them and the genes is that they catalyze the formation of products which are different from themselves, just as inorganic catalysts do. All of them either are, or operate in conjunction with, proteins. But it must be emphasized that these agents do *not* share with genes and viruses the distinction of being independent living units: they are *not* autocatalytic, since they belong to a lower order of complexity.

Enzymes occur in dozens of places in both plants and animals. In the latter they populate the blood, the bony structure, and the liver. Enzymes are found in yeast also, in company with several vitamins. But it is in the digestive system—including the saliva, stomach, and intestines—that enzymes are particularly active. They are especially effective at preparing food for assimilation. They accomplish this by breaking down its tough carbohydrates to simpler compounds, and performing a number of other highly specialized chemical services. An interesting, if extreme, example of what an enzyme can do is furnished by that ill-famed pest, the termite. Since this destructive creature spends its entire life "aged in the wood" and has no access to any other source of food, its stomach is provided with an enzyme which is capable of extracting nutrients from cellulose, a woody material chemically similar to the carbohydrates needed in the body. If this enzyme is removed, the termite dies of starvation. Pepsin is one of the most familiar of these chemical watchdogs in the digestive system of the higher animals.

Since enzymes are produced by living cells, they are

naturally present in the body. Contrariwise, most of the vitamins cannot be formed within the organism. Fortunately they are readily available in almost all fruits, plants, and vegetables, so that it is a simple matter to get enough of them by eating properly, or by taking them in synthetic form if desired. Aside from their direct chemical effect on foods within the body, an important function of the enzymes is to cooperate with the vitamins in fostering growth.

One of the most famous of these so-called biocatalysts is Warburg's yellow enzyme, which was identified in yeast in 1932—a bit of research that resulted in the discovery of riboflavin, or vitamin B_2. The source of this compound is revealed in its name: "ribose," a form of sugar, and "flavus," meaning yellow. In this complex, the enzyme is shown to consist of a protein molecule, to which is attached a chemical grouping containing phosphorus and nitrogen, and later found to be a compound of riboflavin. Here is a case where an enzyme is actually a duplex affair made up of a protein and a vitamin, the latter being the physiologically active member of the team. Indeed, this is true of all the B-complex group. Other vitamins depend for their efficacy on close coordination with various enzymes, and bring about far-reaching changes in the complex chemical transformations that go on within the body. For example, vitamin D owes its claim to fame to its ability to accelerate the deposition of calcium and phosphorus in the bones. Thus it prevents rickets in infants and maintains sound bony structure in adults. It is the one vitamin whose active form is produced within the body by means of sunlight—and this is about the only virtue

of the sun-tanning fad of recent years. Examples of the
physiological effects of enzyme-vitamin activity could
be multiplied almost endlessly; but the point to be
stressed is that these marvelous agents function by
means of catalysis. That they do so is indicated by the
extremely minute quantity required for effective results
—the merest trace is sufficient, except in cases of abnormal deficiency.

Hormones too are protein bodies, which are secreted
by various glands, such as the thyroid, the pituitary,
and the pancreas. The last-named produces the well
known insulin, lack of which results in diabetes. The
hormones have been dubbed "chemical messengers," for
after being released into the blood by the gland which
produces them, they travel to other parts of the body.
Nature sees to it that exactly enough of each kind of
hormone is supplied. The smallest increase or decrease
in this ideal quantity can, and often does, have dire results for the individual, ranging from gigantism to
idiocy, and from extreme nervous activity to complete
sterility. All kinds of distressing and often fatal mal-
adjustments can arise from an excess or deficiency of
one hormone or another. Some of these can be treated
by dosage with externally obtained hormone products,
either extracted from animal tissues or in a few cases
made synthetically.

Probably the infinitely varied action of the many
hormones present in the body is primarily responsible
for what is generally called one's "disposition." The
genes provide our chief hereditary traits, and in general stake out the broad territory within whose limits
our lives are destined to develop. The hormones con-

tinue where the genes left off, and contribute to the fashioning of the detailed characteristics of the individual. Pertinent to this situation is Shakespeare's famous remark that "there's a divinity that shapes our ends, Rough-hew them how we will." Exactly how the hormones work is not known, but it is highly probable that once again a catalytic function is involved. Suffice it to say that they are of just as vital importance to life, growth, and reproduction as enzymes and vitamins.

To summarize this portion of the chapter, we have seen that all the biocatalysts direct and control the chemical and physical reactions and transformations that go on within the cells. They shepherd the basic force of growth, encouraging it here, retarding it there, constantly on the alert for trouble, acting simultaneously as bosses, workers, and planning clerks. It is hard indeed to understand how such an inconceivably complicated machine as the human body can grow, maintain itself, and impart its characteristics to future generations through the medium of these versatile and highly "intelligent" protein aggregates. The seat of this apparent intelligence is the all-pervading catalytic mechanism, which is about as close as scientists have yet come to accounting for the marvels of physiology.

Let us now ascend one flight on the escalator of the imagination to the microscopic level and take a brief look at the cell as a whole. It is conventional to regard cells as analogous to the building blocks of which the organs and tissues of the body are constructed. They may vary in shape—some are almost spherical, others roughly square, and still others long, thin rectangles. The comparison of cells to building blocks will serve well enough, providing that they are visualized as semi-fluid, non-rigid structures rather than as solids.

Bacteria and other low forms of life consist of a single cell—a mere fleck of protoplasm within which are one or more centers of more elaborate organization, which can be made visible in the microscope by staining the organism with a dyestuff. Such centers are called nuclei, and their complexity increases as we proceed from the lower to the higher forms of life. The protoplasm—an extremely complicated colloidal solution of protein substances and water—is contained within a coating which is usually composed of several distinct layers of protein. Tuberculosis bacteria are especially protected by a tough sheath of paraffin wax, making them highly resistant to treatment. Bacteria appear in several distinct forms, among which are long, narrow rods, called bacilli, and spherical bodies, known as cocci. Many of these "germs" have been photographed clearly under the electron microscope (Plate XXI).

When organisms consisting of only one cell reproduce, they do so by splitting themselves into two parts —a process which biologists years ago christened "binary fission," thereby suggesting the name for what happens in the atomic bomb. When this occurs, the portion split off becomes a new organism, which goes on its way and does likewise. Single-celled animals populate unpurified water in astronomical numbers and can easily be observed in a low-power microscope. They have various methods of propelling themselves. Some have tiny whip-like appendages, or flagellae; others are equipped with hairy attachments called cilia. On the other hand, one of the simplest, the amoeba, is enabled to move about by slight variations in the surface tension existing between the coating of the cell and the surrounding water. As a result, parts of the cell become elongated and so are able to enclose and absorb food substances. The fact that every amoeba formed is necessarily a part of the one preceding it suggests the intriguing possibility that a bit of the first protoplasm to appear on earth may be still in existence—that is, if it was undisturbed in its environment by local agencies of destruction, which is unlikely, to say the least.

The nucleus of a cell contains rod-shaped protein bodies, or chromosomes, which enclose the genes, much like beans in a pod. The easiest way to suggest the structure of a cell is to think of an egg: the yolk represents the nucleus, from which the embryo develops; the white of the egg is an albuminous mixture similar to protoplasm, which furnishes nutrients to the embryo; the wall of the cell is represented by the shell. In the case of most cells of microscopic size, this wall is a soft, porous membrane, similar in structure to the parchment filter which Thomas Graham employed in his original dialysis experiments.

This brings us to the point of chief interest for the purposes of this discussion; for it is in the cell walls that colloidal phenomena are chiefly involved. It must be recalled that the cell, as a unit, is thousands of times as large as a colloidal particle. The individual factors which are active within the cells—genes, hormones, and vitamins—have already been described. The cell wall as a membrane, and its effect on the process of life and growth, should now be mentioned.

After food has been broken up by the teeth, attacked

by the saliva in the mouth and the hydrochloric acid in the stomach, and further decimated by various enzymes, it comes to the cells in the form of a water solution containing sugars, minerals, salts, and proteins. Such true solutions, being composed of ions and molecules, are easily able to diffuse through even such an ultra-fine filter as a cell-wall membrane. In so doing they supply the vital factors in the protoplasm with nutrients. The passage of a solution from one side of a membrane to another, a process referred to as *osmosis*, is governed largely by the concentration of the solutions on opposite sides of the membrane; and it is capable of exerting a force which is tremendous in comparison with the amount and fragility of the agencies involved. Osmotic pressure is in a sense the basic factor in growth, which is subsequently directed and controlled by the catalysts within the cell.

When Graham's distinction between the crystalloids of a true solution and the particles of a colloidal suspension was described in Chapter 4, it was stated to be subject to a qualification. It is frequently necessary, for the sake of emphasis, to present the findings of investigators in a somewhat exaggerated way, and to make classifications more rigid and exclusive than they actually are. Too often one forgets that they require modification, with the result that the principles announced tend to harden into ironclad facts which admit no exceptions. This has been the case with Graham's apparently arbitrary division of matter into the crystalline and the colloidal states. It is generally overlooked that he himself stated not that colloidal particles will positively *never* pass through a parchment membrane, but that they *may* do so, though they are "slow in the extreme." Moreover, it is possible for some substances to be both crystalloids and colloids. For example, the bentonite clay which was selected as a typical "hydrophobic" colloidal substance in the early chapters, is found in nature in the colloidal state; but its structure is definitely that of a crystal. In a word, it is possible for a particle to be of colloidal size, and yet be internally crystalline. Viruses and vitamins can also be prepared in the form of crystals.

This is indeed a significant qualification, which tends to blur the distinction between colloidal and true solutions and to lend credence to the fact that, in cases like the diffusion of nutrients through cell membranes, only local conditions determine whether or not colloidal particles can get through to the protoplasm and the nucleus. If the circumstances are right, it is quite possible for a few viruses, enzymes, or hormones to wriggle through the interstices of the membrane and bring about profound changes in the cell, either for better or for worse. This is one reason why infections caused by "filtrable" viruses are so difficult to combat, for they actually penetrate the cells and reproduce autocatalytically.

It is not the purpose of this survey to go into the detailed structure of the cell components and the mechanism of cell division, interesting and important as these matters are. Before concluding, however, the point mentioned at the beginning of this chapter may well be restated, as it has a most important bearing upon any conclusions one may wish to draw about the nature of life. We have seen that the rock-bottom essential for the existence of life is orderly arrangement—a specific fitting together or meshing of the components of matter, in which catalysis plays a major part by virtue of its unique "zipper" property. This being the case, is it not evident that in any living organism, from the lowest to the highest, something more is involved than merely the sum of its atoms? That something is precise, definite structure, induced by catalysis, which in turn is dependent on surface affinities arising from electronic forces—the common denominator of all nature. But order and structure require an external intelligence; it is hardly possible that they are the result of mere chance. It is perhaps beyond the scope of a scientific discussion to imply that there is an intelligence entirely apart from matter, for there is no way of directly proving that it exists, nor of conceiving it in terms of measurable reality; yet the systematic organization of inanimate atoms into acutely conscious, sentient personalities, and the inability of the scientific method to explain life completely in the language of physics and chemistry strongly suggest that it may be so. The entire subject of biophysiology is positively bewildering in its complexity—and when all has been said that man can yet say, there remains the inevitable uncertainty beyond.

CHAPTER 14

Design for Science

o o

o

JEROME ALEXANDER, who for years has been one of
the foremost champions of colloid chemistry, once
likened it to "a stance which we assume, and then tee
off in all directions." Obviously there are other possible
stances which may produce equally good drives, though
none has yet succeeded in making a hole in one, or even
in doing much better than getting the ball on the green.
Not to punish the metaphor further, it is inevitable
that each of the various branches of science interprets
nature from its own particular angle of attack—physics in terms of subatomic particles and energy concepts,
chemistry in terms of atoms and molecules, astronomy
in terms of galaxies and nebulas, and so on. The results
derived do not always agree, and sometimes differ
greatly; yet the total of man's knowledge is advanced
and a clearer perception of the wonder of the material
universe is gained.

The stance, or viewpoint, represented by colloid
chemistry is merely a new way of examining and interpreting the behavior of matter. The purpose of this
book is to acquaint those interested in what science is
discovering with some of the more salient facts about it.
There has been, and should not be, the slightest implica-
tion that colloid chemistry is on the point of supersed-

ing other established sciences. It is simply a somewhat less familiar way of studying matter, which has succeeded in clarifying a number of problems not touched by the more conventional systems of mechanics, physics, and chemistry. Partaking of all three, it constantly merges into one or another of them. It is idle to indulge in any speculations as to the relative "importance" of the physical sciences: the deep truths of nature transcend our facile division of matter into size levels and can only be understood, if at all, on the basis of a comprehensive viewpoint, which correlates the factors at work simultaneously at *all* levels. For example, the physicist may say that the primary, all-pervading fact of the universe is *energy;* the chemist may claim that it is *reactivity;* the biologist that it is *structure.* None of these statements can be regarded as an entirely satisfactory interpretation of the universe, yet each is doubtless correct as far as the "stance" of the individual science is concerned.

We certainly do not feel that the nature of life is rendered crystal clear, and all its knotty problems solved, just because it is now pretty certain that catatlytic action plays a major part in all vital processes. For, probing further, we ask, "What *is* this action, at bottom?" At this point the question has to be turned over to the physicist, who will go as far as possible toward explaining it in terms of electromagnetic forces. So we find ourselves involved in ionic atmospheres, electron orbits, and energy transference phenomena which are quite beyond expression in simple language. And the ultimate answer is far from explicit, for even *those* forces require explanations which are still not forthcoming, and may never be fully and accurately determined. This point is stressed here as a caution against the assumption that the explanations offered in this book are comprehensive and thorough-going, for they are not. They merely attempt to escort the wayfarer to the first stop on the long journey toward truth.

It may fairly be asked to what developments colloid chemistry is likely to address itself in the future. The answer is more or less implicit in the nature of the subject—for it is a point of view which can be applied to a vast range of investigations, of which those discussed in the foregoing chapters are merely illustrative. Almost anything, with the possible exception of atoms and subatomic particles, can be studied with colloidal considerations in mind; and the more familiar one becomes with them, the more extensive become their ramifications. New avenues of approach to many long-standing problems will be followed in this manner—phenomena as diverse as the formation of tree rings, the causes of cancer, and neuropsychiatry.

Thus the advance of colloid chemistry will take place along the ever-expanding front—one might almost say around the perimeter—of scientific knowledge. As we have seen, many of its aspects are by no means completely understood. This is particularly true of the biochemical sphere, in which it is likely that the most fruitful results will eventually emerge. So much is still to be learned about it that all the physical sciences working together will be hard put to it to achieve definitive success. Surely the cancer problem is a pertinent illustration of this point; and there are many others just as

baffling, though fortunately less immediately impera-
tive. For example, there is great economic need for a
reliable method of predetermining and controlling the
sex of farm animals; and studies of the nature of the
aging process in man, with a view to increasing lon-
gevity, are already assuming the proportions of a
science known as "gerontology."

But above and beyond all is the tantalizing possibility
of discovering the inscrutable secret of life—a question
which has tickled the imagination of mankind from
alchemist to Hollywood script writer. Here is the problem *par excellence* for colloid chemists to cogitate and
experiment upon—drawing on other sciences, of course,
for assistance. How to retard the forces which impel us
willy-nilly toward the grave; how to synthesize a living
organism in the laboratory! These are indeed chal-
lenging questions, and it cannot be said that either of
them is in a fair way to be solved in the near future.
Yet if it is so easily possible for chemists not only to
copy but to improve on nature in the field of plastics,
rubber, drugs, and other utilitarian products, why can
they not also synthesize genes, viruses, and living tissues?

We have seen that scientists know that the basic protein complexes which constitute living units consist of
huge aggregations of amino-acid molecules. They also
know that there are at least twenty-six kinds of amino
acids, and that all of these can be made artificially. In
other words, the component parts of the vast jig-saw
puzzle are reproducible in the laboratory. This being
the case, why would it be so difficult to put them together artificially to form a protein molecule, just as

molecules of vitamins, hormones, and previously non-existent plastics have been created? On the face of it this seems like a simple task compared with such achievements of modern science as radio location devices, television, the extraction of magnesium from sea water, and a dozen others. Indeed, we have become so accustomed to having technicians whiff off a miracle or two every few weeks, that nowadays no difficulty appears insurmountable to the non-scientific observer.

This business of making proteins to order, however, is still beyond the capabilities of man: no protein has ever been artificially created—not even the simplest. In nature proteins are formed by plants during the process of growth; but the most painstaking students, among them President James B. Conant of Harvard and Charles F. Kettering of General Motors, have failed to arrive at a full comprehension of the mechanism. They know that it is a catalytic phenomenon in which the chlorophyll of the plant is activated by sunlight in such a way that proteins are formed from the nitrogen in the soil, the carbon dioxide in the air, and the hydrogen in water; but they have never been able to accomplish this feat in a test-tube.*

Notwithstanding our reverence for the experimental method, it must be admitted that there are some cases in which chance plays such a tremendous part that purely empirical efforts are hopeless. No analogy quite

---

* It was recently reported that Drs. Robert B. Woodward and C. H. Schramm of Harvard University have succeeded in combining amino acids into chains consisting of some 10,000 units. They call these chains "protein analogs." Although this work represents a notable advance in the field of protein synthesis, the basic problem is still unsolved.

fits the staggering problem of protein synthesis, but an idea of the likelihood of its being performed can be suggested. If we imagine that the twenty-six amino acids are so many strands of yarn, each of a different color, and that we have an unlimited supply of each color (since all the individual amino acids can be made synthetically), the chance of putting the amino-acid units together to form even a small protein molecule would be like tossing a random handful of the colored strands across the room and expecting them to fall into the design of a Persian rug. It *might* happen—once in a hundred million tries or so; and even then we would have only one simple protein out of the scores which exist, and this in turn would have to be combined with hundreds of others in just the right arrangement before a macromolecule would result. The chances of a design being achieved by this method would be greatly increased if there were some sort of form, or guiding device, which would tend to align the strands as they fell. In nature this function is performed by the catalytic mechanism, but so far at least no one has been able to devise its duplicate.

The colloidal viewpoint will not of itself settle all or even very many of the questions still before us; but it will serve to clarify them, and to provide a fresh and flexible means of interpreting

This world of ours and worlds unseen—
And thin the boundary between.

Index

i

A NOTE ON THE TYPE

The text of this book is set in *Scotch*, a type-face that has been in continuous service for more than one hundred years. It is usually considered that the style of "modern face" followed in our present-day cuttings of Scotch was developed in the foundry of Alexander Wilson and Sons of Glasgow early in the nineteenth century. The new Wilson patterns were made to meet the requirements of the new fashion in printing that had been set going at the beginning of the century by the "modern" types of Didot in France and of Bodoni in Italy. It is to be observed that the *modern* in these matters is a modernity of A.D. 1800, not of today. The "modernist" type-faces of today are quite another story.

The book was manufactured by Kingsport Press, Inc., Kingsport, Tennessee.